PRAISE FOR *THE DEPTH OF HER TOUCH*

"There's nothing more gut-wrenching than to have a child with special needs and not know how to help [them]. In *The Depth of Her Touch,* author Kathryn Carr gives readers hope for children who suffer from various neurodevelopmental disorders. Carr's book is a fascinating look at the MNRI®/Masgutova Method® and the incredible specialist who has reached people in over forty countries with her amazing reflex integration. Read on for a sense of joy and healing."

—Janet Malcolm Hayles, author of *Every Three Hours: A Mother's Story of Raising a Child with Chronic Illnesses from Car Seat to Career*

"A profoundly touching and important biography that is as page-turning and compelling as any bestselling fiction story. *The Depth of Her Touch* provides deep insight into one of the most gifted healers of our times. Kathryn Carr eloquently captures the story of an incredible scientist, healer, and humanitarian whose unique contributions to human health, behavior, and neurosensorimotor development and function will forever change the way we approach human struggles as varied as war trauma and developmental delays. If parents or soon-to-be parents could have easy access to the MNRI® method, we would see far fewer health and developmental challenges in our children. It is my sincere hope that this book gets into the hands of the millions of people who could benefit from the wisdom of Dr. Svetlana Masgutova."

—Beth Lambert, author of *A Compromised Generation* and *Brain Under Attack*; founder of Epidemic Answers and Documenting Hope

"Kathryn seamlessly weaves the complex science of Dr. Masgutova's method with the depth of her heart to tell this incredible story. MNRI will undoubtedly change the way we approach healthcare."

—Monique Farah, writer, director, and documentarian

"MNRI continues to be one of the most powerful forms of therapy I've utilized on my healing journey following the murder of my six-year-old son, Jesse, at Sandy Hook Elementary School. A healing [technique] so effective it does not require thinking or talking about pain . . . mak[es] [healing] comfortable and possible for everyone. MNRI is the future of trauma treatment."

—Scarlett Lewis, founder of Jesse Lewis Choose Love Movement

– THE –
Depth of Her Touch

– THE –
Depth of Her Touch

A Biography of
Svetlana Masgutova, PhD,
Creator of the MNRI®
Reflex Integration Program

Kathryn Carr

Published by Svetlana Masgutova Educational Institute
MasgutovaMethod.com
MasgutovaFoundation.org
MasgutovaGraduateSchool.com

Edited and designed by Girl Friday Productions
www.girlfridayproductions.com

Cover design: Emily Weigel
Project management: Kristin Duran
Editorial production: Abi Pollokoff
Image credits: cover Naida Gazdick, Milkshop Photography; interior photos and graphics provided by Sally Averkamp, Shannon Desilets, Jill Layton, Svetlana Masgutova, Svetlana Masgutova Educational Institute, Isabelle Renard-Fontaine, Milkshop Photography, and Tass News Agency.

ISBN (paperback): 978-1-61966-012-0
ISBN (ebook): 978-1-61966-013-7
ISBN (special edition): 978-1-61966-014-4

This book is dedicated to Dr. Svetlana Masgutova,
and all the children and adults whose lives have been
changed by her and MNRI, including my son, and
the children and adults throughout the world whose lives
have yet to be changed by Dr. Masgutova and MNRI.

A scientist in Russia has always been more than
a scientist in the strictest sense of the word;
he or she has always been a benchmark of morality,
a carrier of culture, and a source of enlightenment.

—Robert B. Lawson, E. Doris Anderson, and Antonio Cepeda-Benito,
A History of Psychology: Globalization, Ideas, and Applications

CONTENTS

PREFACE

FLORIDA, June 2018—Dr. Svetlana Masgutova's fingers bowed and clicked, fluttering over Daniel's knee joint, the femur segment of his upper legs, and quadriceps. She then performed the quick-release technique at precise reflex trigger points, using the Leg Cross Flexion-Extension Reflex*[1] pattern, thereby providing my son with the potential to walk for the first time in his life.

"We call them Kissing Stars, but the formal name is reflex biomechanics and neurosensorimotor regulation points," Dr. Masgutova said. The Kissing Stars are her signature maneuver, a technique inherited from her Russian great-grandfather, whom the family regarded as a village healer.

The Leg Cross Flexion-Extension Reflex exercise is one of the primary reflex pattern techniques she and her family developed during three-plus decades of extensive theoretical and hands-on research. The integration of this reflex is essential for the sensorimotor development, motor planning, and control needed to perform activities such as crawling and walking.

Dr. Masgutova was focused and present as she worked.

Daniel's tension and spasticity settled into a state of relaxation and presence. His body yielded to her touch.

My six-year-old son was born with a genetic disorder: an unbalanced translocation between chromosomes 1 and 8, with a microdeletion of genetic material on chromosome 8 and chromosome 1 containing too much genetic material. He is dependent on my husband and me for his care and survival.

Our diagnosis may have been unique, but as parents, the answers we were looking for were universal.

What were we doing wrong? What were we doing right? Why was our child hurting? How could we protect him? How could we support his development? How could we help him reach his fullest potential?

These were the questions we had been asking since shortly after Daniel entered the world on December 13, 2011, in one of the best health-care systems in the world. He earned high scores on his Apgar newborn assessment; however, he was then whisked away to the neonatal intensive care unit (NICU), where he stayed for six weeks. He was discharged from the hospital after the placement of a feeding tube and a surgery that corrected malrotation of the small intestine.

He had many neurological checkups, of course, but his nine-month was the last one of his first year. Clinical observations from the lengthy report included:

> *High arched palate with cleft of the soft palate. Alert and appropriately interactive. Symmetry in facial movement. Normal elevation of palate. Tongue in midline. Normal muscle bulk, though hypotonia. Good/full antigravity strength and no abnormal posturing on vertical suspension. Briefly bears weight before buckling. Head control incomplete with excessive head lag on pull-to-sit. Unable to sit, even with support. He withdraws symmetrically to light tactile stimulation. On cerebellar examination, Daniel is not yet reaching for objects. There are no abnormal or involuntary movements.*
>
> *Reflexes are symmetrical and equal in both the upper and lower extremities. There are no pathological reflexes.*

In the years that followed, Daniel reached few milestones and fell further behind. We attempted to answer our questions through mainstream and nonconventional means, but Daniel's developmental goals basically remained unchanged from year to year.

Our belief about Daniel's neurodevelopmental status waffled between what could be and what was. By the time he was five years old, some therapists and specialists had prepared us for the possibility, through stilted language, that Daniel may have reached his fullest potential.

We did not want to give up.

We then heard of the Masgutova Method, or Masgutova Neurosensorimotor Reflex Integration (MNRI), a primary reflex integration program intended to support motor, communication, and cognitive development; emotional and behavioral regulation; stress resilience; and immune system support.

I connected with Tricia Borsch, the MNRI parent advocate, to inquire about participating in an upcoming MNRI Family Educational Conference that would be held at the organization's US-based educational institute and training center in Orlando.

Tricia empathized with us, explaining that she understood the fatigue of caregiving and searching for new methods. Her daughter, Holly, was born with an undeveloped corpus callosum—a large, C-shaped nerve fiber bundle that connects the left and right cerebral hemispheres of the brain. Holly spent her first thirteen years in physical therapy, occupational therapy, speech therapy, sensory integration, and social-skills group therapy.

"The therapies helped but did not provide the changes I had hoped for and believed were possible," said Tricia, who also is the founder of the Bridge to Healing Foundation, a nonprofit that provides funding to give individuals with special needs access to therapies and interventions, including MNRI, to help them reach their fullest potential.

Tricia discovered MNRI, or the Masgutova Method, when Holly was a teenager.

"Prior to the conference," Tricia explained, "Holly had poor balance and muscle-tone regulation. Her feet were significantly pronated and lacked motor coordination. Holly had awkward movements, learning challenges, anxiety, poor social and coping skills, and was delayed in processing information. At that point, we were told that she would either need to spend her adult years in a group home or live with me for the rest of her life. After our first MNRI conference, Holly was jumping off a one-foot-high block, smiling, engaged, interactive, confident, and doing jumping jacks and somersaults. Since then she completed a three-year college program that taught her the skills to get a job, keep a job, and learn to live independently. She now has a full-time job and lives a thousand miles from me. I never thought this life path was possible based on her pediatric neurosurgeon's predictions after she was born. As the MNRI parent support coordinator, I quickly realized our story was not unique."

My husband, Dan, and I entered the Svetlana Masgutova Educational Institute for Neuro-Sensory-Motor and Reflex Integration for the first time with our son on a sunny day in June 2018. Flags representing many countries draped the top of the lobby walls. Peer-reviewed journal articles in English, Russian, and Polish occupied a waiting-room table, each exploring the effects of MNRI. These publications also acknowledged Dr. Masgutova's extensive post-trauma recovery experience, including working with evacuees of the Chernobyl nuclear disaster, children who had been badly burned during a train accident in the Soviet Union, survivors of wars and disasters, and families of loved ones who were murdered during the Sandy Hook Elementary School massacre in Newtown, Connecticut.[2]

Other article topics focused on the impact of MNRI on children and adults with different neurodevelopmental challenges, including autism spectrum disorder, ADD/ADHD, dyslexia, nonfatal drowning, hypoxic-ischemic encephalopathy (newborn brain damage), and Down syndrome.

Along one wall, an engraved plaque honored Denis Masgutov as Dr. Svetlana Masgutova's late son and MNRI cofounder.

We met Dr. Masgutova during the early morning of the first day of the conference. We wheeled Daniel's jogging stroller into her office and placed heavy bags filled with diapers, feeding tube equipment, a cooler with nectar-thickening packets, puréed foods, baby spoons, bibs, and laptops onto nearby chairs before we could greet her with handshakes. Meanwhile, Dr. Masgutova kneeled to meet Daniel at his level.

"Good morning and welcome," she said. "How are you, my dear?"

She spent a few moments speaking to Daniel before she stood up and welcomed Dan and me.

"I see your son is very intelligent and curious. He is going to achieve great things in his life," she said.

These words meant a lot. I often had been presented with predictions of what my child would *not* do rather than what he had the potential to achieve. At his six-month-old checkup, for example, our pediatrician said to me, "I would not expect him to be the star student in his kindergarten class." Those words had anchored in me feelings of resignation, doubt, and hopelessness.

We carefully unstrapped Daniel from the baby stroller, which he had outgrown, and lifted him toward the reflex integration "platform." We placed him on the table, and he assumed his typical side-lying position, contracted, as if he were cold.

Meanwhile, Dr. Masgutova began her MNRI Reflex Assessment with a brief explanation of the foundational role of primary reflexes. Primary reflex patterns are the building blocks for human development and serve as subordinate roles to more-complex automatic motor-reflex schemes and learned motor skills. If these primary reflexes do not emerge, develop, mature, and integrate naturally, a child can have physical, cognitive, social, and emotional challenges. If the basic reflex pattern is incorrect, the body will signal a dysfunction or deeper pathology within some reflex pattern component. As a result, the child remains in a state of "negative protection," meaning they continue to exhibit emotional dysregulation or various atypical movements and behaviors.

Much like how a house cannot sustain its structural integrity with cracks or impairments in its foundation, higher-level cortical functions of the brain cannot be functionally accessed without the proper integration of primary reflexes. Therefore, cortical-level interventions are challenging and not necessarily constructive.

"A reflex is an automatic response of the nerve system for a specific stimulus," Dr. Masgutova continued. "We want the response to be proper to age and neurophysiological norm. May I demonstrate what automaticity looks and feels like?"

Her thumb and index finger gently applied pressure to the anterior of my forearm, about one-third of the way down from my wrist, toward my elbow.

"If I press here, you want to close your hand."

My fingers bent forward in their proper automatic response.

"If I press here, you do not. This means I know the point where pressing creates a biomechanical response for the hand to close. The stimulus is tactile and proprioceptive, meaning the stimulus is perceived as a sense of movement and touch. Do you feel this?"

"Yes," I said to her. "I feel that."

Dr. Masgutova evaluated the basic patterns of the reflex according to specific parameters: function of the sensorimotor circuit, sequence and direction, timing and latency, intensity, and symmetry. Daniel's MNRI Reflex Assessment indicated that his primary sensorimotor reflex patterns had varying degrees of significant dysfunction and pathology.

The reflex emergence-development-maturation-integration process could take minutes, hours, days, or even years. The timeline depended on many factors, including

- the person's age,
- diagnosis and other underlying conditions,
- level of the reflex's function or dysfunction,
- traumas or medical problems that occur during the integration journey,
- whether the reflex had previously integrated and was "reactivated" due to a stressful or traumatic event, and
- whether the reflex had not previously integrated.

Dr. Masgutova again allayed our worries with remarks about his high intelligence and the possibilities for gains in his health and development.

"There is no ceiling in the development of a human," she said, referring to the philosophy of world-renowned Soviet psychologist Lev Semyonovich Vygotsky (1896–1934), whose work formulated the basis for the development of the MNRI/ Masgutova Method.

Inspired by the works of Vygotsky and several other pioneering Russian and Western scientists, Dr. Masgutova, during the last twenty-nine years, has developed and refined nonverbal, restorative neuromodulation techniques aimed at improving the functions of the genetically given units of the nervous system—reflexes. The proper function of primary reflexes affects the body's biomechanics, sensorimotor milestones, immune system and central nervous system health, and psychological development.

Dr. Masgutova's MNRI Method has had broad applications.

Our MNRI Family Educational Conference included six fifty-minute sessions specifically designed to facilitate the emergence-through-integration process. One session aimed to activate and engage the first motor reflexes that emerge, beginning in utero. Another targeted the optimal functioning of the skin receptors to help restore lost functions of the nervous system. Techniques designed to support the essentials of human survival, including breathing and eating, composed another session. The last hour involved preparing the body's biomechanics through reflex repatterning exercises.

The MNRI programs Daniel experienced during that first day and throughout the educational conference reduced his reactive responses that were caused by hyperactive reflex patterns and helped release his body's negative state of protection, which was expressed through his body's rigidity and abnormal movements.[3] The techniques awakened the sensorimotor patterns of the body-brain system.

Dr. Masgutova, her family, and an international team of developmental professionals have driven the method's theoretical and practical development. At the time of this book's publication, the organization estimated it had served more than 380,000 children and adults in forty countries.[4]

Dan and I noticed significant changes in Daniel after that initial family educational conference. For the first time in his life, Daniel looked into our eyes. His eyes tracked other people and objects. Instead of keeping his arms folded tightly into his core, he used his hands to protect his body during repatterning exercises that encouraged a plank position using a yoga ball. He began to vocalize and imitate words such as "mama" and "water." He was calm, present, and more engaged with his surroundings.

Other parents and caregivers observed similar changes in their children.

I watched Dr. Masgutova lead an autistic child with severe behavioral challenges in dance. He typed on his iPad that she was the only person who understood him apart from his mother. "I want to stay here forever," his mother said after she read his message to the group.

I observed another child take his first steps, with minimal support, and another who began to vocalize. I listened to stories from the specialists about their own experiences and spent evenings reading through many testimonials written by professionals and families themselves in a book published by the Svetlana Masgutova Educational Institute, *Reflexes: Portal to Neurodevelopment and Learning.*[5]

Why had I never seen anything like this before? What exactly was the Masgutova Method, and who was Dr. Svetlana Masgutova? How could it be that a profound, noninvasive method to facilitate neurodevelopment had not yet reached mainstream application in global health care?

I interviewed families at educational conferences, educational clinics, and educational courses throughout the United States, the Netherlands, and Poland to answer these questions.[6] What brought them to MNRI and how did this method of reflex integration, and Dr. Masgutova herself, affect them personally, professionally, or both? I also interviewed developmental professionals, researchers, and consultants to formulate an objective understanding of MNRI's effect and potential for widespread acceptance.

I had intended for this book to be a biography of Dr. Masgutova, but it became much more than that.

This is a story about the woman who founded this incredible global organization, a survivor of tragic events, including the murder of her youngest sister and the sudden death of her only son. A woman who, despite her personal tragedies, continues to commit her life to helping survivors of stress and trauma, individuals with neurodevelopmental challenges, and people who want to improve their skills and abilities.

This is a story about how her method of neurosensorimotor reflex integration can help children and adults live their lives to the fullest potential—all through movement-oriented therapy and proprioceptive touch.

This is a story about the power of the human spirit.

Above all, this book is a love story.

PROLOGUE

By Accident

Nothing could have prepared her for what she saw.

Dr. Masgutova had spent half her life acquiring the expertise she thought would equip her to help the children who had suffered one of the worst catastrophes in recent Soviet history. Her expectations were derailed in an instant when she faced the aftershock of the train accident near Ufa.[7] About half the more than twelve hundred passengers had died, many of them children. Those who had survived were rushed to nearby hospitals, to wards that quickly became overcrowded.[8]

It was June 5, 1989, one day after the calamity occurred. Children were fighting death and, in many cases, surrendering to it.

The republic hospital in Ufa was immediately reordered into four floors of emergency rooms. Outside, ambulances and helicopters converged on the hospital campus, delivering medical personnel from the United States, England, Ireland, Australia, Germany, and Israel. Firefighters, military, and medical personnel from the Soviet Union swarmed the hospital.

Dr. Masgutova, still tired from an early flight from Moscow, rushed through the hospital doors. White construction paper draped the walls, scrawled with names and dire assessments such as *hysteria, disfigurement, comatose,* and *missing.* Many patients were labeled as orphaned, since their parents had died in the accident. Other names were listed as deceased.

Upon her entry, Dr. Masgutova saw hospital workers stamp the ward wall with more paper, conquering every last inch of clean page with information. A throng of volunteers streamed past her with carts of food, water, medicine, and supplies.

Then she heard wailing from somewhere above. She rushed to the administration desk and identified herself. Dr. Masgutova was one of the first of the twelve volunteer psychologists to arrive.

"Where have you been? No one is helping," the administrator demanded. "We have the medical help, but we cannot stop the children from crying and screaming. Where are the psychologists? Go, now, second floor, go! We are losing time!"

Dr. Masgutova sprinted down the hall and into the elevator. The enclosed lift reached the second floor.

The doors opened to a hell of suffering, crying, screaming, and hysteria. Her breath hitched. Children were wailing in unbearable pain.

Many of the railway accident survivors had died. Those still alive whispered or wailed for their loved ones. Children were encased in linen, some missing their limbs, fingers, or other parts. Some were supported by ventilators.[9] Unblinking, one child sat on his bed, staring beyond the drywall, in a comatose state. Other patients were speechless, exhibiting a deep state of shock. Another child wailed, "Fire! Fire!" while running in circles to nowhere.

A boy shrieked in front of her. He had been standing in the

same spot, repeating the same sentence, hour after hour, as if he were locked in the hours of June 4.

"We were riding with my grandparents, and an explosion happened, and my grandmother had fire in her hair, and she fell down! We were riding with my grandparents, and an explosion happened, and my grandmother had fire in her hair, and she fell down! Where is my grandmother?"

Dr. Masgutova was unsure of how to work with children who had experienced such extreme physical and emotional pain in this type of acute trauma setting. Her expertise was based on working with patients who could access the higher-level cortex of the brain—who could process information, speak, and follow directions. These children were stuck in the brain stem's fight, flight, or freeze response, a barricade to making any kind of cognitive connection. It was impossible to ask them to stop screaming or to comfort them with words. The Ufa disaster demonstrated the dysfunction and pathology in cognition, behavior, and communication that can result in the aftermath of extreme trauma.

She blinked back tears.

Crying was not allowed. This was an unspoken understanding among first responders, although only Dr. Masgutova and one other psychologist were able to abide by this code of professional ethics. The velocity of her thought patterns distracted her from the external release of her emotions.

She closed her eyes and frantically implored her brain and heart to show her a way to bring the children out of their states of shock and paranoia.

Was there a method, a technique, a protocol that she had never tried before? What could she do? What should she do? How could she fix this? How could she help the children recover from such a catastrophe?

Dr. Masgutova thought of a book called *Brain Gym: Simple Activities for Whole-Brain Learning,* by Dr. Paul E. Dennison and Gail E. Dennison. Her program director at the Russian Education Academy had recommended the book to her before she had left for Ufa. She had deposited it into her suitcase during her last minutes of hurried packing.

Dr. Masgutova knelt before the screaming boy. She looked into his frantic eyes and invited his forearm into the cradle of her hand. The tips of her fingers connected with his extended palm. Tracing a shape of the symbol for infinity, she stroked upward from his wrist joint to his elbow, then back down his forearm.

"You were riding with your grandmother," she said, repeating the boy's words. "You were riding with your grandmother yesterday."

She redistributed her touch to his other arm and repeated the stroke, adding a slightly deeper, slower pressure to her gliding fingers.

"You were riding with your grandmother yesterday, and now you are here at the hospital," she said. "You are safe."

She held his hand as if it were glass, knowing that the slightest slip could shatter their connection to pieces. The stroking of his arm and her accompanying words had stirred a sense of surprise and curiosity in him. The repetitive movement and sensation were distracting his stream of hysteria.

"You were riding with your grandfather and grandmother, and now, look, you are here in the room with me," she said.

His outbursts sputtered into silence.

"Yes," he said.

As they stood still, time moved forward, beyond the darkness of 1:10 a.m. on Tuesday, June 4, 1989. This pivotal moment redirected Dr. Masgutova's lifelong purpose.

As it turned out, Dr. Masgutova used a combination of sensorimotor-oriented therapy and a specific depth of proprioceptive touch—tested and refined thanks to a market produce scale—to enable the children to transition from a state of protection and survival into a place of safety, acceptance, and trust.

Amid such chaos, a method emerged with an impact that would reverberate beyond the borders of the Soviet Union and into the lives of neuro-challenged children and adults in forty countries around the world.

CHAPTER 1

Light in the Bashkir Republic

FLORIDA, February 2019—A beam of Central Florida sunlight streamed through the window of Dr. Masgutova's office and illuminated a section of her reflex integration platform.[10] Nearby, I was seated across from her chair.

We were scheduled to begin the talk thirty minutes earlier, but a session with a boy in the next room had taken longer than planned. The child had spastic quadriplegic cerebral palsy, and he was hypersensitive to touch. Dr. Masgutova didn't want to end her work with him until his contracted arms reached a state of freedom from rigidity.

I arranged my pages of questions as she entered the room. She sat down, and I placed the voice recorder across the table. When I looked up, Dr. Masgutova was staring out the window. I suspected she was thinking about the boy.

She turned toward me. "How are you?"

"I am well," I responded.

This first interview occurred several months after our first MNRI conference. Dr. Masgutova's schedule was overloaded; she was always time-compressed. I knew I had to make the best use of her few moments. She spoke several languages, sometimes three within a single setting, depending on which specialists were in the room. The things she said about reflexes and their role in the brain-body system perplexed even some of the most seasoned health-care industry professionals whom I had interviewed.

However, as someone who had profoundly influenced my child's neurodevelopment within the past several months, she was a person with whom I felt I could share some of my personal feelings about my son.

My husband, Dan, and I implemented our post-educational-conference home program on a near-daily basis and continued to see more positive changes in Daniel. His lower body did not buckle when we oriented him in a standing position. His upper body was not as lopsided. He maintained head control for short periods of time during eating. We had begun reducing the amount of nectar-thick gel mixed into his water, and he no longer coughed while drinking.

Daniel also had started to initiate the Bauer Crawling Reflex Pattern.* The Bauer Crawling Reflex activates the corpus callosum, an area in the brain composed of about two hundred million fibers that transmit motor, sensory, and cognitive information between the left and right hemispheres. The Bauer Crawling Reflex is the first motor milestone that requires movement through all three dimensions in space. The combination of three-dimensional movement and corpus callosum activation underscored how imperative reflex pattern integration was.

Even though Daniel was far beyond the age of typical

crawling initiation, the Masgutova Method proposes that each individual should learn how to crawl. We felt overjoyed with the spate of milestones we had experienced in such a short time.

Still, I felt uncertain and vulnerable. At that moment, I relayed some of my ongoing fears about Daniel's developmental delays. What did they mean for tomorrow and the following years? I voiced my worries about being able to take care of him. I felt despair about whether he would love or be loved by a significant other. She nodded and acknowledged my concerns.

Dr. Masgutova briefly closed her eyes. Then she reopened them and leaned forward, ever so slightly.

"I would give anything to have my child back," she said. "Even if he had neurodeficits, cerebral palsy, autism . . . whether he could not speak or walk or had other challenges . . ."

I said nothing for several moments as her words unwrapped her truth. Each of us who can hold a loved one, irrespective of their physical, emotional, or mental challenges, is a beneficiary of life's greatest gift: love.

"I'd like to talk about your upbringing and childhood," I finally said.

"I was born in Russia."

"Where, specifically? Who are your parents, and what was your childhood like?"

"I had very loving parents. I received sunshine from both of my parents," she said. "There is nothing really of interest in my childhood. I don't think there is anything about my childhood that is different from anyone else's. It was a normal childhood."

As a psychologist and scientist in Russia, Dr. Masgutova had access to the concepts and discoveries of trailblazing scientists whose work was largely unknown to the Western world. This knowledge shaped her unique understanding of the brain-body system and the role of reflexes in neurodevelopment. She was born, raised, and educated during one of the most tumultuous and pivotal eras in one of the most powerful nations on earth.[11] The descendant of a village healer, Dr. Masgutova transferred this brilliant knowledge through the gift of a touch that has been described as "unmatched" by many interviewed for this book.

What did her "normal" childhood look like?

The Kirgiz-Miyakinsky District in the Bashkir Republic in the Union of Soviet Socialist Republics was quite bucolic. The western slopes of the majestic, forested Urals, one of the oldest mountain formations on earth, rose along the gentle curves of the open steppe terrain. The Urals long have been a vast and biodiverse wild landscape, accentuated with springs, deep-cut river gorges, crystal-clear lakes, and rare animal and plant life that have sustained the region's people over the past two hundred thousand years. Perhaps more than any area of the Volga-Ural region, the Bashkir Republic's link to ancient life and the earth's early geographical formation was on full display.

Mountain caves presented red-ocher art drawn fourteen thousand years ago, revealing the marvel of human genius in their artistic and advanced technological expression.[12] Thick-walled fireclay vessels, skeletons, neck jewelry, and the belongings of different peoples who claimed the region during its earlier times embellished the shore of a lake during heavy rain.

Centuries of assimilation by different ethnic groups helped define the diverse cultural expression.[13]

By the early twentieth century, the Bashkir Republic was occupied by Turkic Bashkirs, Russians, Tatars, Chuvash, Mari, Udmurts, and Ukrainians.[14] As a result, this historically significant area of Russia has been chiseled and sculpted by ages of cultural and social change.

Indeed, the twentieth century was among the area's most dramatic time periods, forever altering the landscape and the lives of the people who lived through these times.

Bashkortostan was and still is the home of Kim Sadykov and Maria (her nickname was Masha) Sadykova, childhood sweethearts born during the mid-1930s in Bashkir Republic villages in the Miyakinsky District. Life was characterized by scarcity, war, sacrifice, abundance in community, and benevolence. Their Russian culture placed a high value on family, homeland, love, and life. Their upbringing made an impression on the life they created together.

Kim and Masha were raised by older generations who had witnessed the revolution of 1905 and Germany's declaration of war against Russia in 1914. Their elders withstood the Russian Revolution of 1917, signifying the fall of three hundred years of monarchy rule. They braved the subsequent Russian Civil War,[15] from 1917 to 1922, when their region was a major battleground site, and witnessed the establishment of their Bashkir Republic as the first autonomous Soviet Socialist Republic under the new communist regime. The turmoil continued when Joseph Stalin became general secretary of the Communist Party of the Soviet Union in 1922. Millions of people died in purges, famine, and forced labor camps, a major instrument for political repression. Families were pulled apart, and their roots were upended.[16]

Parentless children were placed in orphanages or raised by surviving siblings. This was the case with Kim, who lost his mother, Magira, to war and exile. Kim's father, Gali, a local schoolteacher, died of lung disease when Kim was thirteen years old.

Other parentless children were adopted by neighboring families, as was the case with Masha's mother, Kamal. Masha had six other siblings: some biological and some who were adopted.

When five-year-old Masha and six-year-old Kim met, the world was on the precipice of the Great Patriotic War of 1941–1945, which was considered by local citizens and historians to be one of the most brutal and severe wars ever experienced by the homeland, the republic, and the inhabitants of the Miyakinsky District.[17]

Life for Kim and Masha and their childhood peers reflected this reality. Children were straddled between learning the compulsory, government-sponsored subjects of the day (mathematics, the Russian language, natural sciences, social studies, music, and geography) and becoming equipped for war (battlefield skills for boys and auxiliary nursing for girls).[18] Young pupils were obligated to balance their schooling with caring for babies, toddlers, sick elders, and the wounded in the hospital.

In summer, Kim, Masha, and their peers played hide-and-seek in village fields, long games of *lapta* (a fourteenth-century Russian baseball game), and participated in friendly competitions for the best reader. In winter, their sleds and skis sketched patterns in the snow-coated knolls of the Ural foothills.

Masha and her family supported the war effort by working on one of the district's eighty-six collective farms. The grain, milk, sugar, beets, rhubarb, and other fruits and vegetables produced by the farm were strictly rationed, with the food supporting Red Army soldiers fighting the Nazis.

During these times of scarcity, Masha plucked a crumb of old bread lodged between the cracks of her home's floorboards. Then, clutching the nibble of starch close to her fur coat, she ran out into the milk house, where no one could see her, and licked the dense morsel until it was soft enough to chew. It was a moment Masha would hold on to for the rest of her life: her secret discovery of savoring the simple sustenance for which she had been hungering for years, and that she had finally found.

During those four years, bread, grain, and meat were collected by the tonnage in the Miyakinsky District, along with millions of eggs, tens of thousands of kilograms of feta cheese and wool, and thousands of hectoliters of milk. Gifts of fur coats, quilted jackets, linen, hats with earflaps, felt boots, and tobacco were sent to the soldiers. The villagers contributed money and gold jewelry to the state's defense fund. They gave all they had.

According to local historical records and recollections from Kim, toddlers, children, adults, and elders worked up to eighteen hours each day, without pay, to support the war efforts. Children were left without their fathers and deprived of basic staples, including bread.

Despite the scarcity, people in the village opened their homes and created conditions that supported work for war evacuees, most of whom came from Ukraine, Belarus, Moscow, Poland, and Lithuania. Orphanages were established to house evacuated children.

The shared resilience of survival required Kim and Masha and their community to summon the depths of their inner strength. The difficult circumstances of their adolescence and the loved ones before them shaped their irrevocable commitment to love and the precious gift of life. This was the mindset of the people in the Bashkir Republic who lived through struggle in a homeland they loved so dearly.[19]

Kim and Masha married as political, social, and economic life steadily improved.[20] The leader during the height of the Cold War, Nikita Khrushchev, launched a de-Stalinization policy, one of the most dynamic shifts in Soviet history. This policy had several aspects, including the release of most of the Gulag labor-camp inmates and an easing of state control and repression, a period which is also referred to as "the Thaw."[21]

Kim and Masha moved from Kirgiz-Miyaki to Kujbyšev, a densely populated industrial city about 235 miles away, along the Volga River.[22] Kim studied journalism and education in these two cities (and in Ufa, Kazan, and Moscow).

Masha pursued theater, dancing, and social work, applying those passions to university studies in medicine and culture. However, due to financial hardship, she had to discontinue her medical education. The detour in her professional life was unexpected, as was her pregnancy in early 1958. The couple returned to Kirgiz-Miyaki, where family members were waiting to help raise the new *rebenochek* (baby).

At 5:55 a.m. on September 4, 1958, Kim and Masha cradled their blond-haired, blue-eyed daughter. As the couple spent the next few weeks adoring their newborn, Maya Kimovna, Kim silently felt as though the name Masha had chosen was not one that suited Maya's character. He did not mention his concerns aloud.

When he went to officialize Maya's birth, Kim acted upon his instincts. He returned home with a birth certificate confirming the birth of their daughter, Svetlana Kimovna. The common Slavic female's name, Kim explained to his perplexed wife, was more befitting of their firstborn daughter who, to him, was the physical expression of the name's meaning: *light* or *pure*. At first, Masha was upset with her husband for his impromptu decision. But soon her disappointment receded, as the essence of their daughter illuminated the life of their family and those around them.

Although little Svetlana came of age during what was still a time of political turmoil, economic hardship, and limitations under communist rule, she had freedom in the innocence from such realities.[23] Commentary on the state of affairs in the Soviet Union was not discussed around little ones. The risks of children accidentally revealing unfavorable remarks at school could jeopardize a family's safety. As such, many seasons of her youth were sustained with love, protection, and joy, the qualities of a normal childhood.[24]

Days were filled with reading literature, memorizing poems, and picking herbs and roots in the forest with her grandmother, who shared secrets of her past. As Svetlana acquired an understanding of the world around her, she came to realize that home was less about a house or place. Home was about family, and how you made your place in the world count.

Svetlana's toddler and adolescent years were split between Kirgiz-Miyaki and various cities including Kujbyšev, Moscow, Volgograd, and Ufa.[25] The family's home shifted based on the demands of her father's job assignments and the caregiving needs for her great-grandmother and grandparents in Bogdanovo. During family visits to this neighboring Bashkir Republic village, Svetlana began to work beside her great-grandmother to develop the gift she had inherited from her maternal great-grandfather, who was born and lived sometime between the late nineteenth century and early twentieth century.

Svetlana also became increasingly preoccupied with trying to answer deeper questions about human and natural behavior—with awareness of thoughts, memories, feelings, and actions—as well as the unconscious and the conscious.

The Sadykovs ultimately settled in Kirgiz-Miyaki to build their own family. Kim worked as a journalist at a local publishing house and as head of a school. Masha served as a library systems director. By this time, upward economic mobility was a reality for a larger share of society than during times of war and repression. The scarcity of food and textiles from Kim and Masha's youth was now a memory. The availability of these things was extolled in the form of gifts, and not just on birthdays and holidays.

Svetlana's parents taught her the value of learning in stillness, the gift of comprehension, of empathy in observation, and how one interpreted life around and within her.

"Indifference is not what a human must let into their soul," Kim often said.

These lessons were reinforced on the eve of each Saturday at the dinner table, and at the end of each month, and also on New Year's Eve, which was one of the most important holidays of the year. Kim initiated philosophical reflections on humanity by asking each person seated at the table the following questions: "What did you do for yourself and others? Whose destinies did you change today? Whose lives did you change today?"

It was an exercise toward self-organization and prioritization, but above all, a question of family values. Svetlana cherished the lessons and sought to fulfill her elders' expectations with acts of goodness.

Sundays in the kitchen were a family affair, centered around the orderly procession of making savory meat and potato as well as sweet *pirozhki* and *varenyky.* Masha, Kim, and Svetlana each presided over their own station. Kim ground the dried apples, sour cherries, prunes, plums, and nuts. Masha melted the chocolate. Svetlana carefully rolled out the dough to a half-inch thickness. She was responsible for shaping each circle into a pancake-sized disk of perfection, then crimping the ends together so that the dough of each *pirozhok* remained intact.

Svetlana had a responsibility to keep things orderly, even as a young child. Her sharpened pencils were neatly arranged beside the schoolbooks on her desk table, and the other texts on her wooden shelf were lined up straight like soldiers. Her school bag was also regularly examined for the proper organization of its contents. Each evening, she settled into her parents' bed, lulled to sleep by that day's selection from either her father's library of historic encyclopedias or her Russian children's and adult books. All categories filtered into her daily and nightly reading, particularly poetry by Russian poet Aleksandr Sergeyevich Pushkin (1799-1837) and fables and science stories by Lev Nikolayevich Tolstoy (1828-1910), more commonly known as Leo Tolstoy:

If you magnetize a needle (holding it for awhile over a magnet), and attach it in the middle to a pivot in such a way that it can move freely around, and let it loose, it will turn with one end toward midday (south), and the other toward midnight (north).

When the magnet was not known, people did not sail far out to sea. When they went out far into the sea, so that land was not to be seen, they could tell only by the stars and the sun where they had to sail. But when it was dark, and the sun or stars could not be seen, they did not know which way to sail. And a ship was borne by the winds and carried on rocks and wrecked.

So long as the magnet was not known, they did not sail far from the shore; but when the magnet was discovered, they made a magnetic needle on a pivot, so that it should move around freely. By this needle they could tell in which direction to sail. With the magnetic needle they began to sail farther away from the shore, and since then they have discovered many new seas.

On ships there is always a magnetic needle (compass), and there is a measuring-rope with knots at the stern of a ship. This rope is fixed in such a way that when it unrolls, they can tell how far the ship has traveled. And thus, in sailing in a boat, they always know in what spot it is, whether far from the shore, and in what direction it is sailing.[26]

By late spring 2019, Dr. Masgutova and I already had conducted a series of interviews about her method, both in person, at the Svetlana Masgutova Educational Institute (SMEI), and through email, but we had not been able to go deeper into the story of her childhood until she had retrieved some details from her parents. One morning, I woke up to an email with biographical information, time-stamped around 3:30 a.m.

Soon thereafter, we met at her family home in Florida to discuss the newly acquired information along with additional memories of her youth.

This scheduled interview occurred during a rare day off. A deluge of tasks awaited her attention: editing journal articles, consultations with business administration, developing slide presentations, finalizing educational conference home programs, translations of manuals into other languages, answering an unending flow of email and text messages, and addressing a myriad of both small- and large-scale projects in various stages of motion.

The focal point when I entered her house was a white wall that separated the living room from the kitchen. The wall featured a gallery of three generations of family photos. At the top was a sepia-toned portrait of Kim and Masha in their younger married years. Kim had a dapper, James Dean look, and was wearing a smart, straight-collared button-down. Masha's dark hair was pulled back into a simple bun, and she wore a chevron-patterned dress. They leaned into each other, smiling politely. At present, they still lived in their home in Kirgiz-Miyaki, but they were in various states of health decline; Dr. Masgutova and her family members regularly rotated caregiving, so their parents/grandparents in need were never alone.

The airy, open-floor kitchen was infused with natural light from two-story-high glass doors and windows. The wicks of tea candles flickered beside a framed photo of Dr. Masgutova and Denis.

Warming on the stove top was a pot of fragrant Russian cabbage soup, made with butter, onion, cabbage, carrot, celery, potatoes, salt, pepper, and dill. A dollop of sour cream and a pour of kefir were added for extra flavor and texture. The *shchi* soup was her mother's recipe, she said.

Dr. Masgutova presented me with a small glass jar filled with glistening, golden-colored Siberian honey. My spoon deposited a healthy serving into my teacup.

"A lot of people in our country don't know about their pasts because of repression," she said softly as she sipped her soup. "It is not something we often talk about. Many Russians do not know their roots beyond their parents or grandparents. If they do, they are fortunate. I love my family more than anything, and it is so important that we always remember them and the sacrifices they made for us to be here, safely, together."

Located about fourteen miles west of Kirgiz-Miyaki, Bogdanovo was the home of several of Svetlana's family members, including her maternal grandmother, Kamal; her maternal grandfather, Zarif; and her maternal great-grandparents. In Bogdanovo, she learned of family secrets and acquired ancient healing techniques.

Svetlana and her grandmother Kamal often made early-morning treks across the farmland of the southern forest-steppe, into the cluster of oak, birch, and aspens that hugged the slender Dyoma River. They foraged for herbs, berries, seeds, and roots, which were a main source of sustenance during wars and repression.[27]

Kamal never raised her voice. She spoke softly as they gingerly made their way deeper into the forest. They spent hours here, grounded with nature, the sun suffusing the forest floor with its glow, then, little by little, its light climbing up the sturdy trunks of the trees.

Those early-morning walks were lessons about life, including the unsolved origins of Kamal's own past. She confided what she knew and what she didn't know about her life, things that she otherwise didn't talk about with any of her other children or grandchildren. Of course, she worried about her family's safety, but it was important to shelter her secrets within the heart of her granddaughter, to make sure their family history lived on and that the suffering of previous generations would not be forgotten.

Kamal and her older brother (who died during World War II) were adopted after revolutionary times. They never knew their real names, their birth parents, or where they were from. Their birth parents had been exiled to Siberia for having progressive views that conflicted with the political order. Kamal's father left first. Her mother was sent once she gave birth to their third child. She left on horseback during the winter months, breastfeeding the newborn. Kamal and her brother remained in Bogdanovo. But their parents and infant sibling never made it to Siberia. They died in a snowstorm in the Southern Urals, traversing one of the only pathways to the camps in Siberia. The only tangible link to Kamal's birth mother was a ring with a single turquoise gem that, if sold, could have provided enough money to feed the children for some years. The ring was never sold.

During this winter of exile, various village families alternated weeks, caring for Kamal and her brother until they were permanently adopted into a blended family of mixed nationalities. Those were the years, Kamal explained, when displaced children were often taken to orphanages. Kamal, her brother, and other children were harbored in underground shelters during orphan canvasses, when authorities were going door-to-door searching for parentless children. Despite Kamal's lack of knowledge about her real roots, she and her brother remained infinitely grateful that the

Bogdanovo villagers had taken them in, raising and protecting them.

In the years that followed, Kim quietly searched the available death records for those exiled to Siberia, looking for clues as to the whereabouts of Kamal's birth parents and baby sister. But he could not find the answers, and the circumstances of their disappearance remained a mystery.

While Svetlana and Kamal bonded through long walks, Svetlana connected with her grandfather Zarif's side of the family through hands-on bodywork. Zarif's father—Svetlana's great-grandfather—had passed away before she was born, although he had shared his techniques with his wife. Svetlana spent ample time with her great-grandmother as an apprentice and beneficiary of her great-grandfather's mastery.

This village of about eight hundred was composed of residents who engaged mainly in agriculture, beekeeping, raising livestock, and making carts and sleds. Svetlana's great-grandfather was part of a small group of osteopaths; the family refers to him as a village healer, who was said to have only rested a couple of hours each night. His days, twilights, and dusks were occupied with studying herbs, anatomy, and physiology with a handful of other villagers and also resetting the dislocated joints of locals, who lined up outside his door for relief from their aches and pains. The village group frequently convened, poring over anatomy and physiology texts and putting their studies to practical work. Villagers, weary from the pains of tilling, harvesting, and lugging buckets of well water, lined up to receive the benefits of this group's work.

Svetlana's mother, Masha, spoke of the time he had saved her after she fell into an icy river when she was a little girl. Masha was suffering from hypothermia and could not walk. He retrieved some unfrozen Ural clay from the Okta-Karan River, a tributary of the Dyoma River, in Bogdanovo.

He kneaded the chunks of clay into a makeshift bathtub. He placed some brittle sticks and branches beneath, which he set on fire to harden the clay. Her great-grandfather filled the tub with the icy river water and herbs. The crackling fire below the tub heated the water, which helped restore the function of Masha's joints so she could regain her movement.

Svetlana's great-grandfather also cloaked aching bodies with the hide of a sheared sheep to transfer collagen from the freshly slaughtered livestock for human skin and muscle support.

Svetlana watched her great-grandmother's hands maneuver the bodies of different family members and villagers. Misaligned vertebrae were rearranged back into place with surgeon-like precision, although some instances required a heartier thrust, as if flapping excess water from a freshly washed article of clothing.

To emulate the grace and strength of these ancient techniques learned from family, Svetlana focused on how to develop the fullest expression of her own hands. Each twist, flexion, extension, and bend was reinforced with the wringing of a wet towel or the use of a hand and finger expander.

Click. Click. Click, click, click.

The osteopath group's youngest member's tongue tap-danced against the roof of her mouth as a soap bar plowed into the biomechanical points along little Svetlana's arms, shoulders, and back. A bar of soap was her unique tool for relieving aches and pains.

While the soap worked its way through the nooks and crannies of her body, Svetlana's great-grandmother orbited alongside, using her hands to transfer her late husband's techniques to the body of her great-granddaughter. The tips of her second and third fingers burrowed into the hollow areas under the clavicle, between Svetlana's shoulder and sternum. They circled and stretched in different rotations and various degrees around the clavicle bone, liberating tension from the tendons and ligaments.

The finale was her great-grandfather's Kissing Stars.

Around the same time Masha became pregnant with her second child, a local peasant woman fell ill with heart disease and no longer could take care of her own children. Kim and Masha informally adopted two of the older boys, Sergej and Rafis. Svetlana was seven years old when her baby sister, Nelly, was born.

Svetlana wanted to call her Helen, but her parents named her after a family friend. They assured Svetlana that if they would be blessed with another baby girl, the infant would be given her eldest sister's favorite female name.

Svetlana taught baby Nelly to sketch patterns, knit simple dresses, and make crowns for their dolls, "borrowing" lovely floral fabric from their mother's favorite dress.

The girls spent long summer days pretending and building. They scurried across the yard on their hands and knees with their neighbors, imagining they were beavers building dams. Upon returning from work, their father got down on his hands and knees, cleaning up the strewn yard debris and construction waste, wearily requesting that the girls not manufacture such complicated forts and veterinary clinics. They agreed until the next day.

"Okay," their father said. "If words don't touch your ears, then maybe there is a bigger reason for this."

Perhaps, he mused, his daughters would become the most talented architects or veterinarians.

"Maybe you will even grow to be leaders or doctors," he said.

Eventually, Kim, Masha, Svetlana, and Nelly left Miyaki and spent the next few months living in a rented apartment in

Volgograd (formerly Stalingrad, from 1925 until 1961), along the southwest perimeter of the Soviet Union.

It was a new era in Volgograd's history. Its economic growth was an achievement after the Nazis had reduced most of the city to rubble in an aerial blitzkrieg that initiated the Battle of Stalingrad.

Volgograd had recently been rebuilt from the ground up. Factories and a new oil refinery presided over the banks of the Volga River. Its cityscape was rejuvenated with the construction of Europe's largest hydroelectric station, and new concrete-paneled and brick *khrushchyovka* apartment buildings housed a population boom.

Svetlana's aunt Anna, Masha's older sister, had lived in Volgograd since her teenage years. Anna, like so many other teenage girls, had been recruited to help build weapons in the factories during the war. A land-mine explosion during the Battle of Stalingrad claimed one of Anna's legs, and for a brief time, her ability to work in the factory.

A centerpiece to Volgograd's postwar rebound was the construction of a statue of a woman brandishing a sword in her elevated right hand while her left hand mightily beckons the Soviet Union's sons and daughters to defeat anyone who threatened the motherland. At eighty-five meters in height, *The Motherland Calls* still is the tallest statue of a woman in the world.

Kim, Masha, Svetlana, and Nelly spent many months in Volgograd, supporting Anna with housework and caregiving. While Kim and Masha obliged the early-morning routine of caring for a newborn, Anna tended to Svetlana. Despite the physical difficulties of getting around, she still woke up young Svetlana before dawn. They walked down the street to receive fresh milk-cart deliveries. They harvested sour cherries, apples, and peaches from the garden's orchard trees and vines, and strawberries from the soil, before the sky opened up with the sizzling summer sun.

During the afternoons, the family went to the construction site to witness the elegant and determined statue of a woman rise atop the summit of Mamayev Kurgan. Her determination and strength projected a reassurance that her people would always be protected from harm and invincible to enemies.

To Svetlana, *The Motherland Calls* inspired the ambitions of her aunt, summoning those before her to serve.

These values extended to her adopted brothers. For Sergej, this meant seeing to the protection of his country's citizens, as he eventually would become a major general in the Soviet/ Russian Airborne Forces. His service spanned three decades, between 1976 and 2007, including the Yugoslavia and Chechen Wars, and he earned the gold star of the Hero of the Soviet Union. For Rafis, a builder, the skyline of Moscow would be even more grand with the rise of new skyscrapers.

For Svetlana, Nelly, and later Helen, this call to rise would eventually mean serving those who were sick, vulnerable, or suffering.

IN THEIR WORDS

Patricia Shackleford, PhD, Dean, The Masgutova Graduate School of NeuroDevelopmental Sciences

Svetlana described the suffering children and the profound results they experienced after a Masgutova Method conference.

I set out to prove her wrong.

The changes she had described after a conference in Poland sounded too good to be true. I have been a longtime educator, nationally certified school psychologist, and mental health counselor. I completed my PhD in psychology. I had extensive experience in working with children with significant neurodevelopmental challenges. But I acknowledged that I worked in a field where talking therapy and cortical-driven interventions were the preferred mode of problem-solving, and these modalities were not always effective. It's not that a child with dyslexia does not want to sit down and read, or a child with ADHD should sit still because that is how the rest of the class learns. They simply cannot conform to the same expectations, and there were underlying reasons. I often looked "outside the box" to find help for my students. I held tight to the philosophy that all learners could realize positive changes in physical, emotional, social, academic, and cognitive development irrespective of their challenges.

Still, you don't see the changes Svetlana was describing, at least not without years of work—and possibly, ever.

"We've had children with autism who could speak for the first time after our conferences," Svetlana said to me. "We've had children with cerebral palsy walk for the first time."

Ironically, the reason I attended my first class with Svetlana was not for children. Instead, I was looking for something my special education teachers could use to help relieve the rising stress they faced from administrators, parents, and the increasing numbers of children who identified as autistic or with other challenges.

I attended Svetlana's course on Dynamic and Postural Reflex Integration. I left the four-day course with a basic understanding of how foundational the integration of primary reflexes was for emotional maturity and cognitive development. My husband, Paul, and I even had sponsored some brain-body connection courses and conferences on addiction and other topics in neurology.

We invited Svetlana and her son, Denis, then a teenager, to present new topics based on the Masgutova Method. People from all over the world flew in to this tiny town of fifteen hundred in Bradford County, Florida, because they had heard about Svetlana and the Masgutova Method. She then told me she planned to conduct her first US conference in West Palm Beach, in my home state.

I appreciated the theory behind the method but truly could not believe the success she had told me happened at these conferences, even after I saw the changes in the stress of my teachers and the improvements in their students.

I drove with another fellow educator to South Florida to prove her wrong.

I watched an autistic teenager talk for the first time.

I saw a gentleman who was in a wheelchair because he had been in a head-on car crash and could not wheel himself around. His face was so asymmetrical; one eye was almost an inch above the other. He appeared depressed and lacked motivation for small talk or verbal therapy. On the seventh day of this conference, the gentleman wheeled himself into my room while we had an art lesson. He placed his hands on the table and stood up. The symmetry of his face was nearly aligned. He had a smile on his face.

I was proven wrong.

Since then, I've seen many cases such as these. The Masgutova Method techniques are powerful and assist the body through its innate design to change physical, emotional, and/or cognitive challenges into positive development and life expectations.

Some of my special education teachers said they applied the techniques in their classrooms. Their students were making such gains on their Individualized Education Plan goals and objectives, the school administration and therapists had to schedule additional student-centered meetings to regularly notate the students' progress in physical, emotional, and/or cognitive improvements.

Dr. Masgutova's brilliance in the brain-body connection extended from a lineage of prominent neurophysiologists and psychologists, including many who lived and worked in Russia, advancing their works quietly when government conditions did not favor openness and expression of new ideas.

I always expected Svetlana's work would end up in history books for her scientific contributions.

CHAPTER 2

A Pioneer in the Study of Reflexes

Nine-year-old Svetlana Kimovna scanned the titles of texts and encyclopedias. The floor-to-ceiling bookshelves in a neighbor's home were a delightful repository for historical and scientific literature.

Books on zoology, neurophysiology, neurodevelopment, and psychology and a collection of stories about animal and human consciousness beckoned. Svetlana's curiosity increased as she lingered with each selected read.

In the collection of books were works by several Russian psychologists and neurophysiologists whose interdisciplinary discoveries would eventually inspire Svetlana's graduate thesis, "Unconditioned Reflexes, Unconscious Processes and Personality Perception," and serve as the theoretical basis for her lifelong work in reflex maturation and neurodevelopment.

The concepts and discoveries from these notable scientists

would not be available to the broader global scientific community until years, even decades, after their findings. Due to the prevailing political order of the day, during the early to mid-twentieth century, the work of these scientists remained relatively unknown beyond Russia.

Svetlana withdrew another book from the shelf.

Russian scientist Ivan Mikhailovich Sechenov (1829–1905) had his own questions about consciousness as he contemplated a frog dangling between his pinched fingers by its nose, its spinal cord exposed.[28]

Sechenov's path to this moment had been rather unconventional. His education and family influences groomed him for a career track in military engineering. He served as a field engineer in a Kiev brigade, but his career trajectory didn't suit his passion. Sechenov shifted his interests, and subsequently graduated from Moscow University Medical School in 1856.[29]

Sechenov grew up during the reign of Tsar Nicholas I, a devout Russian Orthodox who believed that God directed his actions. Operating within the limitations of tsarist rule was a risky endeavor for thinkers, scientists, artists, and challengers of conventional thought. A new Russian culture was rising. Literature thrived under writers such as Pushkin and Mikhail Yuryevich Lermontov (1814–1841). Sechenov and his fellow scientists and creatives were in conflict with the tsar, who decided which of their works were published and which would be suppressed.

Sechenov left his country to study and work in the laboratories of different European scientists, including Claude Bernard (1813–1878).[30] It was a golden opportunity to learn beside one of the masters in physiology as a pioneer of experimental medicine in life sciences.[31]

Physiologists of this era, including Bernard, were making strides in unlocking the secrets behind the nature of blood circulation, digestion, metabolism, respiration, and homeostasis. This excited Sechenov. His interest went further and beyond the comfort level of some of his peers and the Orthodox religion. He wanted to know how conscious activity—thoughts, feelings, memories, awareness, and sensations—could be studied by applying physiological methods.

Sechenov was tinkering with a frog's nervous system in Bernard's lab when his scientific psychology and physiology discoveries unfolded.

He exposed several horizontal points along the frog's transected spinal cord. He dipped one of the frog's legs into a mild acid solution and used a metronome to count the number of beats between the dip, or stimulus, and the reflex action. His measurement formed the baseline for a normal reflex action. He carefully pinched a salt crystal between his fingers to stimulate a point along the frog's spinal cord. Again, he dipped the frog's leg into the solution and measured the reaction time with a metronome. In this moment, Sechenov discovered that a disruption, or stimulation, to the spinal cord could alter a normal reflex reaction. He investigated whether stimulation to the brain stem or other areas of the brain would yield the same result.

Sechenov's results further proved the central nervous system controlled whether a reflex action could occur.

This was a groundbreaking notion because the reflex had only been understood as the result of an action that occurred in response to a stimulus, but never in the absence of an action.

Research concerning reflexes was still in the early stages, although its foundational exploration had begun two centuries prior, with French philosopher René Descartes and English physician Thomas Willis.[32] In 1662, Descartes published his thoughts on reflex action and human consciousness, suggesting a duality between "the machine," which corresponded to physical actions, and the "spirit," which was responsible for decisions, judgments, and voluntary actions.

Throughout the eighteenth and nineteenth centuries, scientific studies on reflexes, electrical conductivity, and the nervous system continued. Still, it was Sechenov who brazenly asserted that voluntary movements do not, in fact, differ from reflex movements, as was commonly believed.[33]

Sechenov submitted his findings to a Russian sociopolitical magazine, *Sovremennik* ("Contemporary"),[34] but his article was censored due to its provocative title: "An Attempt to Bring Physiological Bases into Mental Processes." He changed the title to "Reflexes of the Brain," and the magazine relented, publishing it in its lower-circulation sister bulletin, the *Meditsinsky Vestnik* ("Medical Bulletin").[35]

"Reflexes of the Brain" contained some bold and even uncomfortable propositions.

Sechenov proposed a "reflex arc" that represented a three-part explanation of the mind. This continuum of activity permitted nerve impulses to transmit sensory information to the brain and produce a corresponding motor activity.[36] The reflex was the physiological central nervous system unit consisting of a sensory stimulus, a central conscious impression, and a resulting movement. Voluntary movements, therefore, were reflex actions. Reflexes explained complex human behavior and mental functions. Movements and mental functions were influenced by sensory input and motor response and differed only in how the central nervous system managed them, he postulated.

Sechenov declared that principal forms of physiological activity were the result of reflex processes, and that all acts of conscious and unconscious life are reflexes.[37]

Sechenov's assertions were both extolled by Russian scientists, who advocated for an objective scientific approach to psychology, and rebuked by Russian philosophers and censors.[38] The Saint-Petersburg Censorship Committee rejected his article, accusing him of spreading materialism, mitigating the views of Christianity, and corrupting morality.[39]

Private censors took action in 1866, when Sechenov expanded and republished *Reflexes of the Brain.* One year later, the court ruled that no action could be taken against Sechenov because his book did not transgress any law.

Sechenov challenged the overall constraints of the prevailing physiological and psychological approaches, pioneering a regard for objective science over unsubstantiated theories.[40] His work on reflex excitation and inhibition is still central to the understandings of modern neuroscience.

In his book, *Soviet Psychology: History, Theory, Content,* author John McLeish credited Sechenov as shifting a global movement in world psychology away from philosophical analysis to one that applies experimental science and objective methods: "In 1863, he was far in advance of West European thought. The social and political blight of Tsarism had the effect of polarizing opinion: views presented within a climate of compromise, hesitancy, and temporizing in Europe were developed by Russian thinkers to their extremist, logical conclusion."[41]

This time period ushered in the dawn of psychology as an independent science around the world.

In 1891, Sechenov was elected professor of the chair of physiology at Imperial Moscow University, Russia's first and oldest medical university, now named I.M. Sechenov First Moscow State Medical University. He set the stage for future generations of scientists to advance their discoveries, albeit not always within secure and supportive political circumstances.

Sechenov earned a reputation as the patriarch of Russian neurophysiology, inspiring subsequent generations of world-renowned scientists to advance their work amid both repression and the comfort of safety. These life principles inspired the subsequent professional work of an inquisitive young girl: Svetlana Masgutova of the Bashkir Republic.

IN THEIR WORDS

Dr. Nelly Akhmatova, Dr. Masgutova's Sister and MNRI International Leader

I am fortunate to have an older sister, a girlfriend, and a soulmate in front of whom I have no secrets. I can talk with her on any topic that interests me, cry under challenging times, and sometimes be upset and in conflict even when my soul is full. I have shared some of these relationships that connect me with my sister, whom I love and appreciate, and also stay as a rock to support her in difficult times. She is the only person to whom I can entrust all the most valuable and sacred aspects of my life. Whatever situation I may be in, I know I have a harbor, a fortress, where I can land at any time of the day or night and get comfort and support, and share my joy.

My sister was my teacher from an early age.

I remember when I was in first grade, and Svetlana was in eighth grade. We worked through a half page of my mathematics and Russian language homework together. First, she explained everything, and then I trained. I worked diligently, using all my zeal and patience. Thanks to the persistent training of my sister, I was the best student in the class.

Looking back, I am grateful to her for having taught me how to work and how to be responsible for studying. It was believed in my family that if you studied honestly and well, you respected yourself and others. These were principles bestowed upon us by our parents and which we have cultivated in our children.

By the time Svetlana entered her second year of studies at Bashkir State Pedagogical University (formerly Ufa State Education University), she became interested in psychology.

People began to see her potential. She continued to use the healing techniques created by her and based on our great-grandfather's healing practice. She could easily remove a headache or other pain from our mother or aunt by touching a sore spot with her palms and applying special techniques. The neighbors asked her to work with their pain. They left with relief.

I became involved later, and it was a discovery for us, as we were correcting vision and hearing issues using certain exercises. Together, we created stress-release techniques based on breathing methods that we had developed. Beethoven's *Moonlight Sonata* accompanied the exercises. Our first patients were family and friends.

The news of my sister's abilities began to fly around the whole district. For those wishing to have a session with her, despite her very young age, studies, and fatigue, she tried not to refuse anyone.

CHAPTER 3

Lifelines

FLORIDA, April 2019—The teenage boy's eyes followed Dr. Masgutova as her fingertips began to greet his body, starting with both pectoralis major muscles—commonly known as "pecs." She gently pressed into the fan-shaped muscles and paused as she aimed to awaken the body's proprioceptive awareness. She then swept up and around his shoulders and glided her hands down to his wrists, where they remained for a brief proprioceptive stretch. This technique was the first of a comprehensive protocol of MNRI NeuroStructural Reflex Integration exercises that aimed to release tension from the muscles and joints, regulate muscle tone, and mobilize the diaphragm for stress release and improvement of breathing functions. Her techniques addressed the connection between tactility, spindle cells, tendons, and the ligament guard, and the response known as the Tendon Guard Reflex.*

Dr. Masgutova single-handedly created this core MNRI

tactile and proprioceptive integration program during her late teenage years.

A female guardian nearby expressed concern over the boy's chronic knee pain, likely due to the increased patellofemoral forces (pain at the front of the knee and around the kneecap) often present in individuals who suffer from developmental challenges.

"Yes, I know. I feel this through increased tension and in the links between the muscles," Dr. Masgutova said.

She placed both hands on his quadriceps.

Meanwhile, other parents in the conference room changed their vantage points to watch Dr. Masgutova work.

Her hands stretched and squeezed along the muscles from the hip to above the knee. The placement of her fingers targeted specific neurosensorimotor regulation points that activated the reflex patterns to release the brain's overprotection. This touch mobilized the body's receptors, its structure, and its movements into a regulated state of positive protection, or well-being.

Then her hands descended to the peroneus (lower leg) muscles and ankle. It was not just the way her hands moved, it was the feeling one got when watching her, as if there were a change in the air they were collectively breathing.

"I knew by about twelve to fourteen years of age that I wanted to be a body-oriented psychologist," Dr. Masgutova said after we left the conference room and continued the interview in her office.

She clutched a yellow steno notepad, its pages curled back to reveal her most recent sketch—the tendons and joints around the boy's knees.

She flipped the page.

"The traumas of my adolescent years made a big impact. I started to realize the consequences of human suffering."

"How did you manage stress and trauma as a child?" I asked.

Dr. Masgutova drew a bar graph on the blank, lined page. A simple line with a start and endpoint marked the Y-axis. She shaped the X-axis into an arrow. Three hollow bars filled the graph. "This is my father's model for stress. He calls it the Lifelines Model."

She sketched a tulip shape between the first and second bars. "Case number one: stress happened, now let's solve it and release it."

The next U was narrower. "Case number two: it's important to maintain enthusiasm despite a challenge."

Her blue pen dissected the bars with forward slashes.

"These lines are life. Some lines are darker, and some are lighter. How do we prolong the light stripes in life? How do we shorten the heavier times? How do you extend the happy days in life and shorten the negativity? What does the bigger frame of life look like?"

Dr. Masgutova traced from left to right along the X-axis.

"He was always teaching us that this day will pass and the holiday will come to our street. This is an expression in my country. The rainy day will pass, and the sunshine will come back. I understood this model as a way to move past stress. But then I went through the trauma of experiencing the loss of my youngest sister and, later, my first and only child, and everything changed."

Art underpinned daily life in the Soviet Union, including in the village of Kirgiz-Miyaki. Theater and choreography circles played a central role in the village's activities, and the tapestry of creative expression—song, dance, and theater—nurtured inextricable community bonds.

Svetlana's mother's voice lifted those around her, while her grace in song and dance made the synchronized art form look effortless. Svetlana admired her mother's talents in the performing arts and yearned to sing and dance like her.

Village records compiled by a private citizen in Kirgiz-Miyaki indicated that her mother, Masha, played a starring role in professional Tatar theater founder Karim Galievich Tinchurin's *Blue Shawl*, a five-act melodrama written in 1928 that was said to inspire audiences for its plot simplicity, democratic influence, and the beauty of its style of folk song.[42]

Svetlana loved watching her mother move so expressively, both off and on the stage. As a child, she had tried to imitate her mother's theatrical talents but found choreographed steps and rhythms a complicated endeavor.

"You are beautiful as you are, my dear girl. Dance with your thoughts," Masha had said.

Svetlana danced to fairy tales, Tolstoy's lengthy passages that revealed his lifelong concerns with the morality of observing other people's suffering during war, and Pushkin's poems that defended the value of freedom and personal liberty.

Svetlana stopped dancing when she was confronted with traumas during her adolescence, that fleeting stage of life when the purity of innocence is eclipsed by an awareness of the darkness of the human condition.

She saw the physiological consequences of brain trauma when she entered a hospital for the first time, at the age of ten. Her father had invited her to visit his friend, who had been paralyzed from the neck down after a car accident, to see if the cheerful spirit of a child could renew the man's will to live. The experience left an indelible mark. Svetlana was startled by how his body expressed quadriplegia—that he could talk and tell jokes, but his body was devoid of sensation. No amount of pain medication or mobility support could alter his physical state.

"Only one thing can help," he said. "Please sing to me."

Svetlana was ashamed. "I am not a singer. I am sorry."

She recited some poems and then asked whether she could attempt to alleviate his pain through some "exercises" that she recently had been experimenting with on an injured cat.

"Go on and work how you want," he responded. "I do not have any feeling in my body, so nothing will hurt me."

Svetlana stretched an area around the top of the rib cage, between the sternum and shoulder and surrounding muscles, using deep pressure. Next, she pressed along the arch inside the plantar surface of his foot and flexed his big toe. After three repetitions of each exercise, the man's foot twitched, although he said he did not feel the movement.

After subsequent days of exercises, now known as *pendulum* for breathing and stress release and *brachioradialis activation* for proprioceptive awareness and comfort, feelings in his limbs and chest emerged. Svetlana closed and opened his hand, holding each position for seventeen counts. Limb arousal and intermittent sensations of feeling progressed into functional movement throughout the following days.

Svetlana's dad presented a towel-wrapped spoon. The man was able to hold the spoon for a couple of seconds. It was the first time since his accident four years prior that he had been able to perform a fine motor activity.

A few months later, however, the man died. For the first time in her life, Svetlana saw her father cry. She was overwhelmed by her father's outward expression of emotions, as Russian culture disapproved of men crying.

She felt the loss especially through her father's candid grief, and internally questioned what else could have been done to save the man's life.

What was the value of life to the Creator of life?

"We must do everything we can, even place our own life at risk, to save a life until the very end," her father told her. "There is no value greater in this world than life, irrespective of health state."

The brutality of life confronted the normalcy of a joyful childhood, as she later described, when she happened upon a book about the Nuremberg trials and the events that precipitated them.[43]

Svetlana acquired several texts from the local library that described the trials and war crimes. She wanted to stop reading, but could not turn away from the events that came to life on the pages. She read as much as she could about the military tribunals, as if in urgency to uncover the real story—that the deaths of some ten to twelve million people, including people of her own country, were false, a gross, fictional conjuring of events. When she conceded to the gruesome and devastating truths revealed during her readings of the Nuremberg trials, which prosecuted the major Nazi war criminals for their crimes throughout World War II, including the Holocaust, she vowed then never to read about nor watch anything that had to do with torture and murder ever again.

As it were, she eventually would absorb through her own hands the trauma of people impacted by these extreme forms of tragedy.

A deeper calling overpowered her internal pledge, as the realities unveiled the consequences of power, repression, and the suffering of humanity. As an adult, she revisited this truth during subsequent readings about world and national history, including the three-volume, nonfiction *Gulag Archipelago*, written by Aleksandr Solzhenitsyn between 1958 and 1968 and first published in 1973. Like thousands of fellow citizens, she ordered books and journals to uncover the deepest of truths covered up for so long in the USSR.

Svetlana's approaching teenage years signaled a responsibility to determine the path of her higher education. She contemplated fields tied to rehabilitating life and debated how her academic strengths—biology, poetry, and history—converged into a path with purpose. By now, she could read, write, and understand several languages: Russian, Bashkir, Ukrainian, Belorussian, English, German, Bulgarian, and Latin. She also was familiar with Esperanto, an international language created in 1887 by Dr. L. L. Zamenhof, a native of Bialystok, Poland.

Svetlana considered her mother's dream of entering the medical field. Above all, though, the motivations behind human behavior gnawed at Svetlana's consciousness. Her exposure to these first traumas anchored her life's work. After that, she knew how she wanted to dedicate her life's purpose: to alleviate the suffering of individuals and help them transition to a place of healing and new personal growth.

She attended Bashkir State Pedagogical University in Ufa, and during her second year met Renat Masgutov. She was seventeen, and he was five years older, buttoned up in his army officer military dress.

In November 1979, after a four-year courtship, Svetlana Kimovna married Renat Masgutov.

"He had his boots on tight," she could hear her mother saying.

The snow was thigh-deep, and the outside temperature bitter. After the marriage ceremony concluded, and she had officially assumed his family name, they visited the graves of the village's fallen soldiers. Renat removed his fur coat and placed it along the ground, so her delicate high heels would not plunge into the ground.

Svetlana and Renat would love each other unconditionally for the next fifteen years. The first five were spent trying to become pregnant. University colleagues who knew about her private struggles began to suggest she accept her circumstances and abandon her plan for motherhood. She was four weeks pregnant when her doctor delivered the news.

Svetlana and Renat inched their vinyl record player closer to her abdomen at night, playing Beethoven to their unborn child.

CHAPTER 4

Origins

NEW JERSEY, April 2019—"The moment I held him, I looked into his eyes. I told him I would love him unconditionally. He looked back into my eyes as if he understood me. I told him I had waited a thousand years for this moment. Then he was taken away from me," Dr. Masgutova had said the previous night, during another interview. "It would be ten days before I would see him again."

I sat with about fifty other students in her newly developed MNRI Introduction to Intronaut and Infant Reflexes Integration course, held at a New Jersey hotel. As I watched her prepare to begin lecturing before a packed conference room, I contemplated our parallel experiences of having our newborns taken unexpectedly from our arms.

Touch is one of the most complex, multilevel, and multifunctional senses. Millions of bits of sensory input reach the brain through the skin. During a natural birth, intense stimulation of all skin receptors takes place. A mother then holds her newborn child for the first time, strengthening their bond and creating a feeling of safety. We both had missed out on the full essence of this experience.

I chose to attend this newly developed course to better understand the theory behind the MNRI/Masgutova Method. Indeed, any of the forty-plus courses offered through the Svetlana Masgutova Educational Institute provide theoretical and practical concepts of the method through the lens of each subject's particular focus—Archetype Movements, NeuroTactile, NeuroStructural, Dynamic and Postural Reflex Integration, Stress and Trauma Recovery, and Children with Challenges among them.

This MNRI Introduction to Intronaut and Infant Reflexes Integration course explored the significance of primitive and primary reflexes,* beginning at conception and lasting throughout the prenatal and postnatal period. This course was a linchpin in Dr. Masgutova's MNRI concepts. The MNRI proposes one of the most unique and productive concepts of working with expectant mothers, newborns, and infants during this neurophysiologically sensitive time frame in human development.

"Primary reflexes have specific purposes in utero and after birth, until they finally integrate and serve as subordinate roles to more complex sensorimotor schemes," Dr. Masgutova explained to the class.

In the case of a neurotypical infant, using MNRI to support growth and development at the beginning of life eases the transition from aqua-uterine reflexes to air and ground reflexes. This type of early intervention optimizes protection and strengthens the nervous system, creating a solid foundation for future growth.

In the case of a baby born with challenges, using the MNRI

techniques at the beginning of life provides the possibility of shifting an abnormal developmental trajectory and rerouting it onto a more neurotypical path.

Reflex integration is foundational for human development and survival, from the birthing process to the last heartbeat; however, reflex integration programs are not widely used throughout life.

The modern, mainstream approach to infant screening is said to be lacking in its ability to address neurodevelopmental red flags comprehensively and quickly. In the United States, *early intervention* is the term used to describe the therapy and educational services and supports available for families with babies and young children who have developmental delays and disabilities.

Infants and children with prolonged post-birth hospitalizations may transition directly into the program upon hospital discharge. Still, infants born without immediate concerns are not referred into the program until developmental issues arise during well-baby checks. Even then, there is typically a wait-and-see approach, delaying the beginning of services.

The MNRI Reflex Screening, MNRI Reflex Assessment, and reflex integration programs aim to facilitate more-effective early intervention by building upon a healthy neurological system and supporting natural development. The MNRI approach addresses potential future red flags by working with primary reflexes within seventy-two hours of birth. In addition, MNRI targets underlying neurology rather than focusing on treating symptoms and diagnoses, which could lead to compensatory habits.

"Our research has shown that 50–60 percent of cases can be significantly improved if early intervention starts at birth, along with physiotherapy," Dr. Masgutova said. "This is the window in which the neurosensorimotor circuits can be most effectively switched on, revealing the fullest expression of the reflex, its role in sensorimotor coordination, and overall brain development. We propose reflex integration as a foundational interdisciplinary approach to healthy support of the whole person, from the prenatal period and throughout life.

"We do not see problems. We see possibilities," she said.

What exactly are primary reflexes, and what role do they play in our conscious and unconscious sensorimotor system development? What are the implications of an immature or nonintegrated reflex on a child's quality of life? What are the consequences when an integrated reflex has been reactivated due to a traumatic event?

These questions have formed the foundation for the comprehensive theoretical and practical application of Dr. Masgutova's reflex integration programs and curricula.

Her transformational method has appealed to a wide swath of professions and backgrounds, including health-care and wellness personnel, psychologists, teachers, massage therapists, nurses, occupational therapists, physical therapists, infant specialists, speech and language pathologists, feeding specialists, developmental ophthalmologists, audiologists, and parents like me who are searching for deeper answers regarding the role of reflexes in a challenged child's development.

Dr. Masgutova began that day's lesson with an overview of selected MNRI theories and concepts.

A reflex is an automatic motor response to a particular internal or external stimulus. Reflexes are neurological building blocks, influencing brain functioning and higher-level physical, emotional, and cognitive development as a person matures. Reflexes also serve as the body's protection in stress and survival.

Her explanation was derived from the basic understanding of a reflex as a physical response of the brain, theorized by Sechenov and Russian physiologist Ivan Petrovich Pavlov (1849–1936), and this more advanced physiological explanation of how it works from Pavlov and Sir Charles Sherrington (1857–1952), an English neurophysiologist:

- Sensory receptors within various body systems, such as tactile, auditory, visual, vestibular, and proprioceptive, detect a change in body homeostasis.
- An afferent sensory neuron sends a message through the spinal cord to the brain stem, relaying the information.
- The brain stem interprets the sensory information and determines the appropriate response.
- An efferent motor neuron directs the response message to the proper body system. This could include skeletal and/or nonskeletal muscles, depending on the desired or necessary response.
- A motor response is generated.

The work of Dr. Masgutova and her international MNRI team is based on viewing the reflexes as central nervous system units and then using those units to springboard to healthy protection, stress resilience, immunity, neuroplasticity, and development.

Conventional therapeutic methods aim to treat challenged children by addressing the higher-level functions found in the cortex. But a child with delays in speech and language development cannot say "Mom" or "Dad" without a solid foundation that was built when they were younger by primary reflexes such as suck-swallow-breathe, Babkin Palmomental,* Robinson Hands Grasp, and Head Righting.

MNRI shifts the focus of the childhood educational and developmental strategies to supporting the subcortical brain structures and the extrapyramidal nervous system.

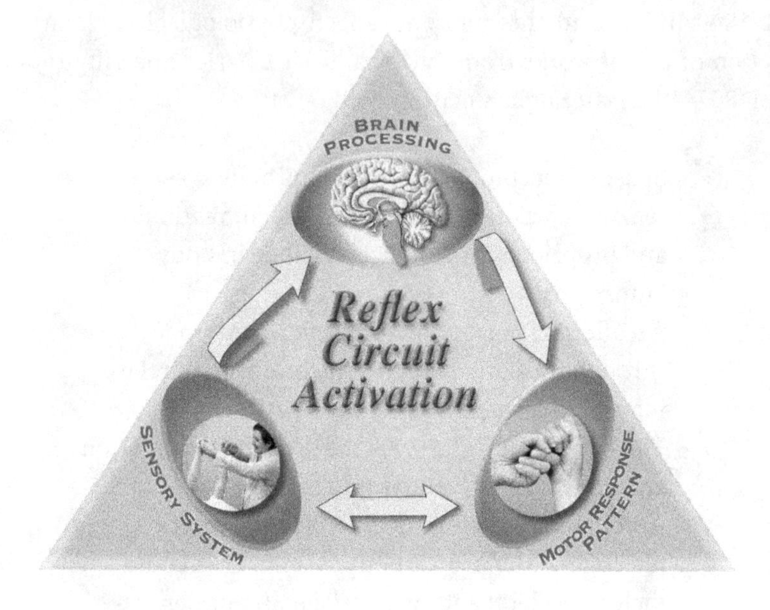

The Journey of Reflex Integration

Each child is born with a complex system of natural responses referred to as primary sensorimotor system reflexes. They are genetic programs of human development.

This complex system begins developing at conception. A stimulus such as touch or temperature change can elicit two responses within the newly formed cell: expansion, when the stimulus is desirable and supportive, and contraction, when the stimulus is limiting or threatening. These two tiny responses will eventually develop into the more complex response of whole-body flexion and extension. Flexion can provide a momentary pause or freeze to assess the unsettling situation or provide the ability to lean in and fight.

Extension provides the ability to flee the threat, also known as flight.

By about four weeks of gestation, the neural tube along the baby's back closes. The baby's brain and spinal cord develop from the neural tube. The embryo can flex and extend along this central line. This incredible movement activates lower-level (survival and instinctual) and higher-level (conditional and rational) brain functions.

The first motor patterns, called archetypes, appear at six to seven weeks. Archetype patterns include movement of the spine and limb buds into flexion and extension; spinal rotation, which divides the body into upper and lower halves; vertical shortening and lengthening of the spine; lateral flexion-extension of the spine; and three coordination patterns—homologous, homolateral, and cross-lateral—for using the limbs together as a team.

These movements will lay the foundation for the reflex motor responses and, later, intentional, controlled movements.

By the eighth week of pregnancy, the embryo becomes a fetus and begins to look more human.

At nine weeks of gestation, the ability for withdrawal into flexion splits into two branches that will become the Fear Paralysis and Moro Reflexes: Fear Paralysis for freezing and Moro flexion for fighting or curling up to protect the vital organs. Moro extension provides the flight response.

Beyond the ninth week in utero, the baby begins to suck and swallow. They can hear their mother's heartbeat and voices outside the womb. A loud noise will startle them.

By twenty-three weeks, their sense of movement is evolving. Their reflexes have emerged and will continue to grow through the third trimester. Development continues a rapid-fire trajectory during the last couple of months in utero as the brain-body systems and functions mature. The intronaut (fetus) can grasp and play with the umbilical cord and turn their head toward skin-filtered light. They can kick, roll over and spin, suck and swallow amniotic fluid, cry, smile, and dream.

The primary reflexes that are trained in utero are "activated" during the birthing process and immediately after, for the first few months of life, as the infant adjusts to life in this very different environment. Once that adjustment is complete and the baby understands breathing, touch, gravity, feeding, eliminating, and so forth, the reflexes take on the role of development. However, protection and survival will always be their number one priority.

Each reflex begins in a basic pattern that is unconditioned and automatic, but with time and repetition, it will eventually mature into an integrated pattern that is purposeful and controlled. This journey involves seven phases.

The first three phases "code" or create a pathway for the reflex circuit to connect the sensory stimulus to the motor response, just as Sherrington described. This connection takes place in the brain stem.

Phase four is a transitional phase in the diencephalon part of the brain, which is the bridge between the brain stem and the cortex. During this phase, the baby gains the control needed to move out of the reflex response.

Variations of the motor response and full control are acquired during the final three phases of reflex integration, which occurs in the cortex. This is where learned motor patterns become functional to achieve developmental milestones. The reflex is now conditioned and fully integrated.

Conditioned reflexes support the development of intentional and specialized functions controlled by the brain's left and right hemispheres so that we can rationalize, reason, think critically, organize, socialize, or otherwise perform higher-level skills and actions that are functional and goal-oriented.

If the integration of primary reflexes matures as nature intended, all three brain levels—the brain stem, the diencephalon, and the cortex—will work interdependently, as one coherent system.

Grasping the Concepts

For the class to further understand the concept of a reflex's journey from emergence to integration, Dr. Masgutova projected a slide of the Robinson Hands Grasp Reflex.

Robinson Hands Grasp emerges during the eleventh week in utero, setting the stage for a baby's eventual ability to grasp an object. Holding and exploring objects set the stage for cognitive development, according to Dr. Masgutova's interpretations of Vygotsky's concept of reflex development, so this reflex is important for other developmental areas, in addition to motor skills including cognition (grasping a concept) and inner strength (having a grip on a situation).

The basic, primitive first phase of Robinson Hands Grasp begins with the thumb inside the fist. During phase two, the thumb finds its way outside the closed fist and rests in front of the fingers. This is a critical transition for establishing and anchoring the circuit of the reflex pattern. This also is the only phase during which myelination is theorized to occur. It also shows that after ten days of life outside the womb, the newborn is beginning to adjust to this new life, and stress levels have diminished.

In phase three, isolated movements of the thumb merge, and it comes to rest on the side of the hand against the index finger. The rudimentary reflex pathway in the brain has now been created.

Phase four transitions into the diencephalon, where the baby is learning how to move out of the reflex pattern. The palm begins to open, although the fingers are still curled for now. Like most transitions in life, it is an emotional change.

Given the position of the hand, which is perfect for hanging from a ledge, this phase is referred to as "hanging grasp" and is another position frequently seen during MNRI Reflex Assessments when stress levels are high and the client is "hanging on for dear life."

It is here, in the diencephalon, that motor and emotional control are learned.

A disruption in the development of this stage of the reflex eventually could lead to emotional outbursts, inappropriate or impulsive behavior, or repetitive actions. Certain habits may improperly form. Memory will be affected. The regulation of neurotransmitters and the balance of stress hormones will be impacted. Developmental skills will function at a low level, causing even more stress and quick fatigue.

During phases five through seven, neural networks are developed, and the reflex completes its maturation process. There is proper coordination between sensory input neurons, the motor response neurons, and the interneurons, which play an essential role in the balance of excitation and inhibition for motor control.

Robinson Hands Grasp movement is now intentional and taking place in the cortex, so babies and toddlers can point for communication, poke, pinch to pick up tiny objects, and hold a crayon with three fingers.

If this reflex does not integrate properly—or in other words, all seven phases of the pattern are not experienced and matured—the child may have trouble gripping a pencil, or conversely, they may apply excessive pressure on a pen or pencil because their fingers are involuntarily flexed. They may want to avoid handwriting or other fine motor skills. Lacing shoes or buttoning shirts may be difficult. The child may also have difficulties with speech articulation and communication since the hands and mouth are closely linked.

Reflexes truly are the most important units of all life.

Problems with an Improperly Developed or Immature Reflex Pattern

An integrated primary reflex no longer elicits a robust and evident response from a stimulus, since the unconditioned reflex pattern has matured into its conditioned version. Nevertheless, primary reflexes are activated during moments of stress or danger, when a person is most vulnerable to losing their controlled thought processes and must rely on automatic responses for self-preservation. Simply put, a person cannot think or respond rationally when they are in major stress or survival mode. Since the cortex is unavailable, the primary reflexes in the brain stem take over.

A nonintegrated primary reflex does still elicit an automatic response to its sensory stimulus. This impedes the brain's ability to regulate the proper levels of excitation and inhibition, which disrupts the control of purposeful movement. The child's brain stem is constantly activated in protection and survival, and the reflex's priority cannot transition into developmental mode.

Improperly developed or immature reflex patterns can manifest as social anxiety, laziness, poor motor functioning, problematic behaviors, speech delays, exaggerated emotions, cognitive challenges, and more.

What Are the Reasons a Reflex Does Not Integrate Properly?

There can be problems with any part of the reflex circuit that inhibits integration. Hyper- or hyposensitivity will prevent the reflex from being properly stimulated. Poor body symmetry, archetypal movement, or muscle-tone regulation will prevent a proper reflex response. And any damage or stress to the brain can prevent the two pathways from connecting to each other. The reason is frequently a combination of these issues, which is why Dr. Masgutova has created techniques that address all possibilities. This is why Dr. Masgutova is considered a leading global authority on reflex integration.

But why would these problems arise?

There are numerous reasons why a reflex may not follow its proper developmental profile. Genetic issues such as chromosomal abnormalities, stress or trauma in utero, and birth injuries are some of those causes.

A pregnant mother's stress can influence the integration of her unborn baby's reflexes. Studies have shown that when an expectant mother suffers prolonged stress, her stress hormones release into her bloodstream and cross the placenta to the baby—which increases the risk of that child developing a mental or physical illness later in life.

Infancy is incredibly distressing as newborns adjust to their new environment and need to survive. High levels of stress hormones during infancy can damage the development of the neurotransmitter systems and, ultimately, brain development, leading to possible delays in reflex integration and neurodevelopment.

Babies and toddlers spend less time on the open floor and more time in swings, reclining chairs, and playpens. Play tends to be more structured. Their increasing dependence on screens reduces gross motor activity and affects their ability to achieve quality, healing sleep, increasing the risk for attention deficits, stress, anxiety, depression, and other health problems.

Based on forty years of practical experience and supported by a deep bank of reflex data that she has accumulated since 1989, Dr. Masgutova has theorized that 90–95 percent of modern babies are born without properly functioning primary reflex circuits. Through scientific research, education, and practical work, Dr. Masgutova has advocated for the essential tool of reflex integration in early intervention for all babies, beginning right after birth.[44]

Even with early intervention, circumstances can happen later in life that cause the reflexes to waver, such as prolonged stress or trauma (physical or psychological).

Additional issues may be tied to the stresses of our modern, on-demand lifestyle. The proliferation of ultraprocessed foods, chemicals in the environment, and other external disruptions may affect the quality of reflex integration.

Primary reflexes will reemerge and get in the way of purposeful movement patterns, memory, control of emotions, sleep, and executive functions, requiring a reflex integration "tune-up."

Without interventions, these symptoms could possibly lead to post-traumatic stress disorder, which would require more work and time to reestablish a sense of normalcy.

Universal Application

The specialists in the MNRI community believe that every individual on this earth, irrespective of age, can benefit from neurosensorimotor reflex integration. Tens of thousands of people worldwide already have because of the work initiated by Dr. Masgutova, Dr. Nelly, and Denis.

Dr. Masgutova concluded the first day's nine-hour lecture and hands-on practicum.

I expected the students to stream toward the exit doors, eager for a walk in the freshly mowed spring grass outside or anxious to hail a ride-sharing service that would have transported them to a nearby restaurant.

After a full day of MNRI theories, concepts, and question-and-answer sessions, the students' curiosity should have been satisfied, at least for the day.

Instead, the students wanted to know more, and a long line began to form. This interaction was demonstrative of the more technical and philosophical questions that Dr. Masgutova and her international team had been researching: What roles do neuroplasticity and myelination play in the transition of a reflex from its unconditioned to conditioned state? What happens during the process of maladaptive blockage to dynamic changes in a reflex circuit?

How can we redefine the approach to early intervention? How can reflex integration gain more widespread acceptance as an effective modality for early intervention and lifelong support of health? How can a whole-child model of care that includes MNRI be advanced to reduce the effects of childhood chronic health conditions?

These questions have been integral to Dr. Masgutova's research since 1989, the pivotal year in which her trauma recovery volunteerism in Ufa precipitated years of life-changing research and practical work.

IN THEIR WORDS

From professionals who participated in the course

Isabelle Renard-Fontaine, Pediatric Physical Therapist,
NICU Specialist, and MNRI Instructor and Core Specialist

The impact of the neurosensorimotor reflex integration method is optimally powerful at the very beginning of life. I have worked with more than twenty thousand babies, and I repeatedly see the changes with the early intervention of the MNRI during this sensitive time frame of neurophysiological development.

I often tell this story through a baby born with amniotic

band syndrome, a rare congenital disorder attributed to the anomalous amniotic bands that entangle fetal body parts during intrauterine life. In her case, the abnormality was located at the superior third portion of the baby's right arm, near her shoulder. The microvascular surgeon performed an immediate post-birth surgery. Occupational and physical therapies were initiated at eight and ten weeks post-surgery.

Six of the primary reflex patterns, including Robinson Hands Grasp, Babkin Palmomental,* and Asymmetrical Tonic Neck Reflex (ATNR),* were determined as pathological or deeply dysfunctional during the initial assessment of the reflex patterns.

For the first ten weeks of this infant's life, no evident activation of the right biceps had ever been observed despite the traditional OT intervention. However, active right elbow flexion movement repetitively occurred after we performed the MNRI repatterning technique for ATNR. The repatterning techniques awoke the inherent sensorimotor-memory resources without any direct inputs to the arm.[45]

After ten months of MNRI-based therapies, substantial improvements were noted. The techniques integrated the upper limb and spinal reflexes, and the infant gradually recovered the function of her arm from the proximal to the distal segment. She began reaching gross motor milestones, including balancing on her tummy, rolling over from back to belly (and vice versa), sitting, and commando crawling. At the age of five, she began gymnastics and was able to do cartwheels with the arm that initially had been the subject of a discussion for amputation.

I have twenty-five years of experience as a pediatric physical therapist and have spent the last ten working with Dr. Masgutova and MNRI. Before I took my first course on Dynamic and Postural Reflex Integration, I was still somewhat skeptical about the significance of reflex integration in human development. The more I understood and referred to the MNRI theory and principles and applied the techniques with newborns and babies in the NICU, the more the method's effect seemed to be validated.

It was amazing to watch how the Spinal Perez Reflex* pattern could unlock a tight sacrum and pelvis in an infant born through C-section, who otherwise had missed the proper activation of this reflex since the infant was not able to be born through the birth canal. I also observed the monitors showing how the NeuroTactile Reflex Integration techniques clearly regulated the babies' heart rates and respiratory rates during moments of stress in the NICU environment.

I attended my first MNRI Family Conference as the accompanying physical therapist for one of my clients.

This young girl's parents had provided Dr. Masgutova with only very minimal medical background information in the pre-assessment registration paperwork. In addition, she had no formal medical diagnosis. The little girl was verbal, but she didn't say a word.

Dr. Masgutova explained to the child's parents that putting the consonants *S* and *K* together was challenging for the girl due to her dysfunctional oral reflexes, her low facial muscle tone, her atypical tongue position, and the lack of activation of cranial nerves V, IX, and XII. I knew this little girl could not pronounce the word *school* properly. She would say "ksool" instead. I had never seen a professional accurately assess articulation skills without hearing the child talk.

Dr. Masgutova performed a cursory check of the degree of mobility in the pelvis, knees, and ankles as well as a further reflex assessment of the Automatic Gait, the Trunk Extension,* and foot reflexes. Based on the level of integration of these reflexes, Dr. Masgutova identified significant challenges with walking. A hyposensitive and hypoactive Babinski* meant poor foot stability. A dysfunctional Leg Cross Flexion-Extension

Reflex Pattern resulted in a lack of leg differentiation and poor advancement of the limbs with each step. Dr. Masgutova determined the nature of the girl's emotional and behavioral challenges as a result of the mixed responses between Moro and Fear Paralysis.

She could determine the girl's gait deviations just by evaluating the direction of the Spinal Perez Reflex. She did not need to see the child talk or walk or perform a specific task.

As PTs, we are formally trained to assess the gait pattern by observing the client walking. We take notes about how the foot is oriented, the hips' excursion, the knee's alignment, et cetera, as the child performs the functional task.

By assessing reflexes, Dr. Masgutova collects information regarding the possible causes of the symptoms observed versus just observing the symptoms themselves. The MNRI Reflex Assessment enables her to build a plan of action describing the necessary techniques to start the reconstruction of reflex training work.

Within a thirty-minute MNRI Reflex Assessment, Dr. Masgutova pinpointed a full picture of the girl's personality traits and talents, and her physical and cognitive challenges, without having any prior information. The child had breakthrough gains in the eight-day conference that followed. From that point on, I understood the seriousness and the validity of this method.

▲

Yichien Su, Speech and Language Pathologist with Expertise in Pediatric Feeding Disorders, PhD Candidate, and MNRI Instructor and Core Specialist

From a scientific perspective, I was intrigued by MNRI after seeing some of the changes in my clients after participating in this modality. From a personal perspective, I needed real answers about why my Samuel's genetic condition was missed at birth. He had infantile spasms and chromosome 7q deletion, and he died in my arms at sixteen months old.

One of my earliest MNRI clients was a girl born with a malformation of her brain's right hemisphere. She had spent most of her early developmental years in a medication-induced fog due to ongoing seizure activity, so her developmental progress was glacial. Doctors prepared the family for a future where the girl would be fully dependent upon them for lifelong care. Crawling, walking, and talking were beyond the realm of possibilities. After her second brain surgery at the age of three and a half, the child began receiving MNRI. She started to use language in a meaningful way, including making word approximations to request something she wanted and demonstrating early problem-solving skills.

I have been frequently asked, "Will MNRI cure my child?"

This is not the question to be asking.

If a child has such medical complexities, they may require certain equipment, such as a feeding tube for life. Because the medical system is structured the way it currently is, I typically first see these children after the feeding tube has been placed, and way after that neurophysiologically sensitive time frame of seventy-two hours after they are born, when an MNRI Reflex Assessment and integration strategies can be most effective.

If you can help a child diagnosed with pediatric feeding disorder come to a point where they can safely taste and swallow food, you have opened a door for real bonding for both the child and the parent. Feeding is a foundational bonding experience. Additionally, swallowing opens the door for higher-level developmental skills, such as vocalization and speech. It is about giving your child the best chance at quality of life and helping them realize their highest genetically given potential that is innate in every one of us.

My introduction to MNRI paralleled the pursuit of my PhD. I began to study the role of primary reflexes in neurodevelopment on a much deeper level. I developed my thesis around the relationship between breathing, swallowing, and oral-motor reflexes, a subject about which there is little understanding and research outside of MNRI. Our current understanding is limited to the presence or absence of primary reflexes and whether they indicate pathologies. We remain uninformed in the maturation progression of primary reflexes and their crucial roles in children's development and individual well-being.

Available treatments for pediatric feeding disorders include compensations via adaptive feeding tools, methods, and modification to food consistencies. While some are effective in bypassing underlying pathologies, they are not adequate at addressing the neurodevelopmental needs for our children to move beyond survival and progress successfully into their development.

I am passionate about the MNRI modality from a clinician's perspective, and I empathize with the pain and unanswered questions from parents who have children with challenges.

The current medical system is geared toward survival and is not focused enough on early intervention and developmental needs that can improve quality of life in the most meaningful and proactive way.

▲

Trina Deiss, Trauma Recovery Specialist,
MNRI Instructor and Core Specialist

Every MNRI experience is incredible. Two immediately come to mind that speak to the depth of the impact MNRI has had. We were providing recovery services, including the MNRI trauma recovery protocol, for a community on behalf of a nonprofit that provides trauma-informed care and training for adoptive parents, educators, social workers, and victims of human trafficking. We had been notified that a woman had spent twelve to fourteen hours traveling by bus and foot to try and reach us when she heard we were providing MNRI post-trauma recovery work with this particular community. We were tired, but of course, we could not say no. She had been trafficked, so we took her through the MNRI post-trauma recovery protocol. We worked with her for hours, well into the early morning of the following day. When we asked her to visualize a place where she could find peace, she answered the middle of a desert, because she could see anyone coming at her from different directions. She was a lot more at peace after our session.

Within that same weekend, we also met a young teenage boy. Four other men surrounded him to help keep him calm and keep my staff and me safe. He was hypervigilant. His eyes were scanning his periphery, and he was breathing heavily. We requested that only his translator and mentor stay. We gently told him we wanted to help him. I asked him if it was okay if we took his hand, and he nodded.

We invited the boy to lie down on the table. I applied light pressure to his pendulum points (beneath his mid-clavicle), and he just started sobbing somewhere from deep within. I started doing Fear Paralysis (tapping techniques to release negative emotions), and my daughter used the Embrace Squeeze technique on his legs. His mom had been a prostitute, and when she was working one night, she came home to find the boy's little sister dead. He had been left as a young child to take care of his sister. We don't know what happened, but his mom blamed him, beat him, and kicked him out. He had a lot of scars, as if he'd been cut. He was homeless and prostituted. He was six years old when he was rescued. We finished his post-trauma protocol—just one session—and he gave my daughter and me the sweetest, most visceral, thank-you hug.

Somewhere, deep from within, it seemed he felt free.

▲

Diane Whiteside, Physical Therapist,
MNRI Instructor and Core Specialist

I was treating a three-year-old boy with cerebral palsy when I first heard about Dr. Masgutova and MNRI. The boy's mother demonstrated the child's poor muscle tone by showing me how he could not continually press the push bar of a water fountain while taking a drink. His movements were dominated by active reflexes. Traditional physical therapy techniques were not working for his motor development. The mother attended two MNRI classes and asked if I was open to the theory and learning this method. I agreed. That experience put us on a profound path of learning and healing. We began integrating MNRI into the boy's traditional physical therapy. He is now twenty-five years old. You probably would not know he has cerebral palsy if you saw him walking down the street. His movement patterns are refined, and he has conscious control of his body.

I recently worked with a child who constantly was on antibiotics for bladder infections. After just three MNRI sessions, her immune system became more regulated, and she has been infection-free and off antibiotics for six months now. As a result, the child's motor coordination for cross-lateral movements has improved. She is on a swim team, and her swimming speed has accelerated. I've applied MNRI to children who toe walk, and it is remarkable to see improvements in their gait pattern and emotional regulation after just a few sessions.

I have been amazed by the global effect of reflex integration on the children I work with. MNRI does not just improve physical motor regulation and coordination development. This modality helps with the regulation of emotional and cognitive development and immunity. I love that parents can learn the techniques and have something simple and tangible in their hands to help their child. I never imagined traveling worldwide, teaching this incredible program, and seeing life-changing results in children and adults. You heal yourself every time you help a beautiful life. This is the same feeling I have when I am with Svetlana. I reach my highest potential when I am with her.

CHAPTER 5

Life Is Movement and Touch

FLORIDA, June 2019—I stood in the back of the room to observe the closing ceremony of a five-day MNRI Post-Trauma Recovery Conference.

The participants were children and adults who had suffered different traumatic events. The closing ceremony gave the participants the opportunity to describe the outcomes they had experienced within themselves or their children.

One mother stood up to describe the changes seen in her son and daughter, who had been adopted from foster care. She began to speak, but she had to stop as she started to cry.

"Kylee initiated the Moro stage 3 reflex pattern for the first time last night," explained SMEI cofounder Pamela Curlee on her behalf.

This third and final phase of the Moro Embrace Reflex

Pattern is characterized by the intensity of an embrace that is an inflection point in bonding and body symmetry.

The significance of this response might have been imperceptible to the casual observer, but it was a tectonic milestone between a child who could not unbind from her trauma and a loved one so deprived of this mutual affection. Initiating a hug meant that Kylee was setting free of the fight-or-flight protection mechanism of survival. She was opening up.

When it was his turn to speak, a burly father wearing black jeans, a leather motorcycle vest, and a ball cap cleared his throat. His voice trembled as he described how his wheelchair-bound son had sat independently the previous night for the first time.

A mother who had flown from halfway around the world was there with her autistic adult son.

"You saw him during the first day," she whispered. "He was cupping his ears and flapping his hands. But yesterday, for the first time in forty-one years, he opened the car door for me."

People who represented different nationalities, cultures, and socioeconomic circumstances conveyed similar reactions around the room.

Pamela and Dr. Masgutova spent the next hour or so answering questions and saying goodbye to families and children at the MNRI Post-Trauma Recovery Conference. Pamela then continued to work with specialists on post-conference educational training. I accompanied Dr. Masgutova back to her office. The late afternoon glow provided the space with natural light. The environment was apropos for the forthcoming reconstruction of her trauma recovery work in Ufa.

We were scheduled to talk about Ufa and Chernobyl. Specifically, what differentiated the post-trauma recovery protocols.

Her phone buzzed four times and then dinged with a new message. The clock ticked.

She glanced out her window and watched as two lean sandhill cranes fluttered their wings and pranced on the lawn.

"They always come to dance when the children are here," she said before she eased into her office chair and faced me.

"The work with Chernobyl victims was more organized, systematic, and long term," Dr. Masgutova said, "unlike the real-time, first-response work required of the Ufa catastrophe.

"The victims of the Ufa catastrophe had phobias. If they saw someone outside their hospital window light a match, they automatically thought an explosion or an atomic bomb would follow. Their lineal thinking was correct, and their comprehension was proper. But we couldn't say, 'No, that is not so.' Words were not helpful. My first discovery with Ufa was to talk less. We did not want any kind of talking therapy during an acute stress state that could revictimize the survivors.

"On a physiological level, the survivors of the Ufa railway accident were in stress and shock. Transmarginal excitation was happening in the nervous system—arousal from constant stimuli about danger and pain. Sechenov was showing us this in *Reflexes of the Brain*. The brain cannot handle overexcitation. The brain must self-regulate or it goes crazy because of unbearable sensation from stimuli, yeah?"

I had my list of well-rehearsed and predictable questions ready to ask about the difference between the circumstances of the Ufa and Chernobyl trauma recovery work: What were your primary discoveries in Ufa? How did you help release the states of negative defensive responses of the central nervous system and establish a sense of emotional recovery, healing, and safety for the children in Ufa? Which reflex repatterning exercises did you initially discover, and what results did they demonstrate?

But the role of transmarginal excitation and inhibition in the stress response must be sufficiently explained before a proper compare-and-contrast could be appropriately contextualized. The recorder was rolling, yet I spent the next fifty minutes furiously scribbling her explanation, a challenging feat, given the complexity of the topic. The role of excitation and inhibition in the stress-sensitive areas of the brain was just one, albeit fundamental, aspect of a complex neurophysiological process of the body's reaction to extreme stress. This high-alert, red-alarm response state helps us understand why a child or adult may experience the acute and prolonged symptoms of traumatic stress, including panic attacks, phobias, hypervigilance, intense memories, nightmares, unstable gait, labored breathing, withdrawals, passiveness, and disassociation that the children in Ufa had demonstrated.

Stress is part of every person's everyday life. The human body is equipped to manage normal stress responses with the genetically given resources of the body.

The autonomic nervous system controls and regulates the internal organs without conscious effort, and this system comprises the parasympathetic and sympathetic systems. American physiologist Walter Cannon (1871–1945) revealed that the body's autonomic nervous system manages two general states of body function: the non-alarm state and the alarm state.

A healthy individual who endures an isolated traumatic event will experience a normal activation of the neural responses generated by the sympathetic system. These impulses travel from the lower brain to the organs and tissues, causing automatic bodily responses such as increased heart rate, rapid breathing, and trembling.

The HPA (hypothalamic pituitary adrenal) stress axis releases ample adrenaline and cortisol levels during this sympathetic system stress response. Under negative stress, reflex reactions mobilize "freeze" or "fight-flight-fright" responses. Each organ, tissue, and cell in the body is activated when a stressor disrupts the body's homeostatic status. Changes in the nervous and endocrine systems occur.[46]

If the parasympathetic system can regulate the stressful excitatory processes in the brain-body system, then the person can resume the non-alarm state.[47] They can breathe easier, reorient to the priorities at hand, and continue with the day's activities.

During overwhelming fear, stress, or trauma, the body can shift into a state of transmarginal excitation. The brain's cortex cannot voluntarily control this state. The parasympathetic system releases neurotransmitters and hormones in larger volumes to help the body pause and relax. This genetically encoded process helps prevent brain-body-system damage. If the amount of neurotransmitters released is insufficient, the HPA stress axis releases more stress hormones. An excessive release of these chemical messengers and stress hormones may prompt a reaction of shock, which can cause transmarginal inhibition. Proper interventions must be applied to calm down the body; otherwise, a person can collapse or disassociate from their body.

"We don't want this," Dr. Masgutova said. "The over-excess of these stress hormones is poisonous to the nervous system. If we are activating the HPA stress axis repeatedly without getting enough time to go back to a non-alarm state, the body will become used to the maladaptive stress mechanism and will unconsciously remain in a state of alarm."

Hungarian Canadian endocrinologist Hans Selye (1907–1982) revealed some of the complications of the stress response. If the sympathetic system remains predominantly in control, without permitting the parasympathetic system to return to its normal state of regulation, then the body can sustain internal physiological damage.[48] When stress is overwhelming or becomes too difficult for a person's genetic programming to handle, acute stress disorder (which occurs immediately after a stressful event) or post-traumatic stress disorder (the long-range effect from a trauma) can occur.

Acute stress disorder can cause painful flashbacks and nightmares. People relive the event or may feel numb in their daily lives.

More persistent stress states create a low-level trauma to the body that triggers primary reflex patterns to resurface, whether in children or adults.[49]

"Intermittent, prolonged, or chronic stress can weaken stress resilience. These stress states can cause dysfunctions in primary sensorimotor reflex functions," Dr. Masgutova said. "During the first part of the reflex circuit, poor sensory stimuli transmission due to poor electrical conductivity of sensory neurons can disrupt processing in the brain stem at the interneuron synapses with an abnormal release of neurotransmitters to the motor neurons. During the last part of the reflex circuit, poor electrical conductivity in the alpha motor neurons or gamma motor neurons that affect muscle fiber movements can cause dysfunctional motor responses."

Translation: the reflex circuit diminishes under stress.

My pen scrawled through several pages of my Moleskine notebook. I ended up listening to this recorded interview five times and transcribed the recording word for word. Previous interviews with high-level seasoned health-care professionals had revealed similar situations. Many of them have taken Dr. Masgutova's courses, such as Dynamic and Postural Reflex Integration, several times to absorb her concepts of the role of primary reflexes in neurodevelopment, stress, and trauma.

"We needed to establish normalcy as much as possible in the Ufa situation," Dr. Masgutova said. "We needed to distract the brain from pain."

She asserted that trauma can only be released by working with the nonrational, nonemotional automatic responses that originate in the nerve networks of the reflex system in the interbrain, where the basal ganglia, thalamus, amygdala and insula, and limbic system reside.

"These areas of the brain govern the emotions, reactive responses, and movements associated with the body's alarm state," she said.

Her phone buzzed again. She reached to silence it. I glanced down at my recorder, which notified me that it had archived nearly an hour's worth of material.

"What was the first lesson you learned while treating the children in Ufa?" I then asked.

"The first lesson in Ufa was to create something on a non-verbal level that can talk to the brain to change reception and distract from pain. Instead of using words, let's talk to the brain in a different way," she said. "The children from the Ufa catastrophe were in such severe pain that they didn't want to play. So we exchanged play with movement-oriented therapy and touch, to help distribute the excitation."

IN THEIR WORDS

Pamela Curlee, Cofounder and Head of Instruction,
Svetlana Masgutova Educational Institute

I formally met Svetlana after the first day of her first United States educational conference, which was on movement-oriented therapy and reflex integration. Her mastery went beyond the how to the *why*. It was a wealth of scientific information that was impossible to fully comprehend.

She introduced herself and made three simple statements: "In Russia, we have excellent results with children with learning disabilities using reflex integration. I teach psychology in Moscow and volunteered in Ufa to help with psychological recovery for many children after a historic train catastrophe. Through our work, we have experienced excellent results by teaching children with cerebral palsy how to walk."

She was sincere and matter-of-fact. Her statements were simple, but I knew they were supported with vast knowledge and human experience. I was intrigued. I knew there was so much more to her method.

At the time, I had been working as a faculty member of the Educational Kinesiology Foundation.

I enrolled in the Dynamic and Postural Reflex Integration and Archetype Reflex Movement Integration courses. I attended additional conferences where Svetlana was a featured lecturer. She invited me to work at the organization's third MNRI Family Conference, held in Poland. I spent more than a month there. The conference work was preceded by several days of intense hands-on training in NeuroTactile Integration, NeuroStructural Reflex Integration, certain reflex repatterning exercises, and the theory of neurosensorimotor reflex integration.

Svetlana, Denis, and I hoped a couple of local families would attend. Instead, the demand exceeded their expectations. The initial conference drew about a hundred families, with others who signed up to be on a waiting list.

There were a lot of core specialists from Poland and new specialists-in-training from the United States and other countries. We all witnessed the most amazing developmental transformations in children.

I watched Svetlana perform the pre- and post-conference assessment of reflex patterns for a boy with cerebral palsy. He had made some significant gains, but she knew how to activate certain reflexes at his post-conference assessment and help improve his integration score. I was so moved as I watched her because she so deeply believes and shows us how we can reach the highest potential, the highest version of ourselves. I had never seen that depth of connection before.

The children made incredible gains in their milestones. Their parents just cried.

I said to Svetlana and Denis, "These MNRI conferences have to come to the United States. We need more doorways to bring this method to the world."

I invited Svetlana and Denis to my home in Colorado. We spent days at my kitchen table, sketching out the vision for what would become the Svetlana Masgutova Educational Institute for Neuro-Sensory-Motor and Reflex Integration. A brilliant and complex method, the MNRI/Masgutova Method is also quite simple and profound.

Svetlana, Denis, and I were like Johnny Appleseed, planting apple seeds in different countries. We were not sure where and even whether we would grow. The Masgutova Method initially took root here in Florida, then throughout the Midwest, West, Northeast, the Netherlands, Indonesia, Singapore, Australia, and of course, Poland.

During the first ten years of our working relationship, I continued to encourage Svetlana to tell the story of how she discovered the method—that is, the railway catastrophe in Ufa. She declined every time. It was far too painful for her.

I respected her wishes, but told her that this story needed to be shared at some point. She could have retired after this one event and had a powerful story of trauma recovery work that would live on for generations. Instead, she continued to grow and develop her method with the goal to bring her knowledge and healing to the world.

One night, Svetlana agreed. She and I worked all night long. I typed as she spoke. There were pages all over the floor. In 2004 we published *You Are a Winner,* which described how children who were recovering from shock and hysteria could return to strength, courage, and inner wisdom through a method Svetlana created in real time during her volunteer trauma recovery work.

Dr. Masgutova's great-grandfather, considered to be an early twentieth-century healer in a remote village in Russia, and her great-grandmother, who shared his techniques with young Svetlana.

Young Svetlana with her father, Kim, and her mother, Masha, in the Bashkir Republic.

As a child, Svetlana became increasingly fascinated with human and natural behavior. While she initially contemplated a career in the medical field, her interest in body-oriented psychology led her in a different direction.

Svetlana's late sister, Helen, was studying to be a psychologist before her life tragically ended. Children loved her whimsical and effervescent personality.

From left: Nelly, baby Helen, and Svetlana.

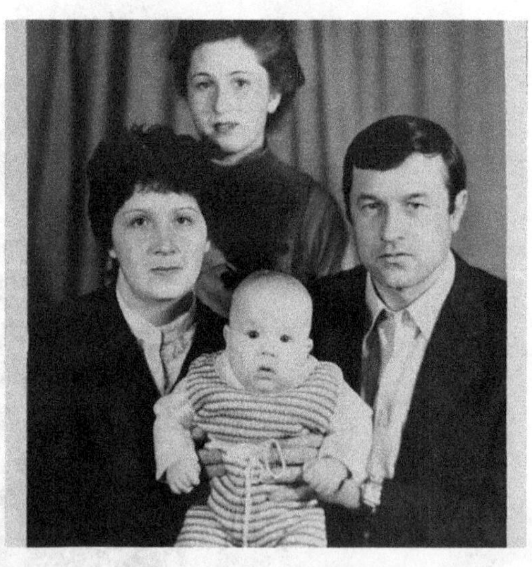

From top, clockwise: Nelly; Dr. Masgutova's late husband, Renat; baby Denis; and Dr. Masgutova.

Relatives and friends visit the railway accident zone, where two passenger trains, No. 211 Novosibirsk-Adler and No. 212 Adler-Novosibirsk, crashed on the Ulu-Telyak-Asha running line of the Kuybyshev Railway in Iglinsky District on June 4, 1989.

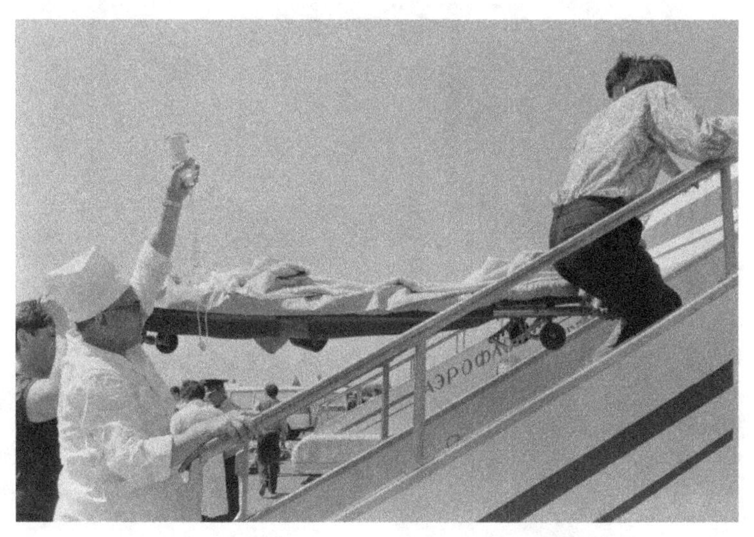

Victims of the railway accident—many of whom were children—are flown to nearby hospitals. Dr. Masgutova was one of the first of twelve psychologists to arrive at a republic hospital in Ufa. Her volunteer trauma recovery work consisted of sixteen-hour days lasting four and a half months.

Citizens check the list of victims hospitalized in Ufa, Chelyabinsk, and Kuybyshev after the railway accident in the Bashkir Republic. Dr. Masgutova recalls the walls covered with reams of paper, listing the names of the deceased and survivors.

Dr. Masgutova's late father, Kim, a journalist, interviews survivors and witnesses of the Ufa railway accident near Ufa.

CHAPTER 6

June 5, 1989

The accident occurred at around 1:10 a.m. on June 4, 1989, about thirty-two miles east of Ufa.[50]

A twenty-car train had been transporting young students from the coniferous forests of Siberia to a camp at Artek in the Crimea, a peninsula on the Black Sea. The camp was a reward for these pupils, who had excelled in their academics. There were also several families on the train's passenger list, heading to Adler, also on the Black Sea coast.

At the same time, another train had departed from a station near the Black Sea and plied through the Ural Mountains. Its seventeen cars were filled with parents, children, and their relatives returning from a seaside sojourn. The two trains were scheduled to pass as they traveled through a valley near Asha, 750 miles southeast of Moscow.

The trains propelled toward each other on parallel tracks. From the conductors' windows, all seemed well. Unbeknownst to them, the ravine below was a deadly bowl of heavy methane vapor.

A pipeline carrying liquified petroleum gas from the distant oil fields in Nizhnevartovsk to the refineries in Ufa had ruptured. Rather than investigate the drop in pressure, operators cranked up the pumps, pushing fuel into the ravine below. The liquefied natural gas was a mixture of propane, butane, methane, and benzene. When combined with air, it became a cocktail for combustion.

As the two trains approached each other, a shock wave equal to ten thousand tons of TNT catapulted eleven railcars into the air. A cloud of gas flambéed the atmosphere, erupting more than three miles into the sky. The explosion demolished an entire section of the Trans-Siberian Railway. Railcars were crushed and charred. Twenty-six cars burned within ten minutes, seven of them incinerated beyond recognition by the blast of 1,800-degree heat. More than 150 acres of trees were destroyed, and the explosion shattered windows in dwellings up to seven miles away.

Hundreds were killed in an instant.

One locomotive expelled one of the engineers. His limbs were broken and his skin burned, but he managed to crawl a couple miles to the nearest village for help. The conductor and his assistant saved more than three hundred lives by organizing an immediate rescue from the burning train.

Nearly half of the twelve hundred passengers—a third of whom were children—perished in the explosion and the fire. Those who survived were rushed to nearby hospitals.[51]

The catastrophe sent shock waves throughout the Soviet Union. Head of state Mikhail Gorbachev suspended the inauguration of the new all-union Congress of the People's Deputies, a watershed event that signified a tilt away from the ideals of a one-party communist state and toward democracy. He declared a national day of mourning, imploring his people to pause their lives to honor the hundreds of dead and dying.[52]

The news made international headlines. The *New York Times* published a piece on June 5, 1989, on its front page: "500 on 2 Trains Reported Killed by Soviet Gas Pipeline Explosion."

When Dr. Masgutova heard about the railway catastrophe, she immediately offered to help. To her, volunteering was a moral imperative, a calling that echoed the lessons bestowed upon her by ancestors, many of whom were casualties of the government's purges.

Dr. Masgutova's childhood home had been a sanctuary for injured cats, stray dogs, hedgehogs, and even injured wolves. When she was little, she found a bird on the banks of a swamp, its legs bent unnaturally, like broken toothpicks. She gingerly cradled the bird. "Please, Daddy," she had said. "We need to take the bird to the veterinarian and save its life." They took the bird to the village veterinarian, who suggested returning it to the swamp and leaving it in peace, where it should die as nature intended. From that day on, she wanted to become a veterinarian.

Her family didn't just rescue animals. Dr. Masgutova's childhood home also served as a temporary shelter for a battered mother and her child. When the woman's husband figured out her location, he arrived in the middle of the night, notching gashes in the front door with his axe.

Never one to back down, Svetlana's father moved the family to a back room and opened the door. His calm but firm demeanor extinguished the inebriated man's rage. He quelled the man's anger and sent him away, ordering him never to return.

"We must always rise above those who try to steal the inner peace of an innocent life with their cruelty," her father said. "You must always help someone who is in need or cannot speak for themselves. You must help anyone vulnerable until your very end. Do you understand?"

"Yes, Daddy, I understand."

It had been about eight hours since the train accident occurred. Dr. Masgutova notified her scientific leader at Orekhovo-Zuevo State Educational University that she would be leaving shortly for Ufa. She secured her train departure and arranged for Renat and Denis to arrive a few days later.

Dr. Masgutova recently had finished her doctorate at the Scientific Research Institute at the Russian Education Academy. Upon graduation, she was hired as faculty dean of the Practical Psychology Department at the Orekhovo-Zuevo State Educational University (Moscow district) and lecturer at the Moscow State University of Education. She had spearheaded the establishment of twelve new department programs, including Dynamic Psychology, Neurolinguistic Programming, Psychodrama, Symphonic Psychology, and Body-Motor-Oriented Psychology.

During the journey, Dr. Masgutova's mind careened through different strategies, based on her experience, for dealing with the crisis. She contemplated Gestalt therapy, a form of psychotherapy that would invite the child to describe their feelings in the current moment rather than focusing on the past. Freud's psychoanalysis presented the opportunity of releasing the child's anxiety by applying therapeutic techniques to make the unconscious conscious. This therapy would require multiple sessions, in which she would sit out of the survivor's sight so that they were free to express their thoughts and dreams, while she inferred which were the unconscious conflicts that caused each child's symptoms and problems. But the volume of the caseload coupled with the medical team's pain management protocols could make this proposition tricky. Art therapy was another possibility for reaching children at their level, extricating them from the accident's terrors and into a safer state of mind.[53]

The natural-cultural psychological concepts of Vygotsky anchored Dr. Masgutova's preparation.[54] According to Dr. Masgutova's interpretations of Vygotsky's concepts, if a child entered the world without any genetic abnormalities or significant trauma or stress, their natural physiological process would mature as nature intended. They would have deeper interactions with the world around them as they advanced through all periods of childhood crisis and transformation.[55] This biological pathway of human development was the blueprint toward achieving one's highest potential.

What were the consequences of periods of extreme, acute stress on childhood? How would the impacts of extreme, acute, or post-traumatic stress affect a child's ability to reach their highest potential?

It seemed logical that some of the tools and techniques that served the victims of the Chernobyl nuclear disaster could be applied to this situation. Moreover, a combination of these programs could help the damaged children move beyond their traumatic state and into a place of safety.

Dr. Masgutova summoned that work to the forefront of her mind.

Three years earlier, a series of mistakes during a safety test had resulted in a reactor meltdown at the nuclear power plant in Chernobyl. The resulting fire had exhaled a plume of radioactive material into the environment that contaminated a swath of land across the western Soviet Union and much of Europe, putting millions in danger of radiation exposure or sickness.[56]

At that time, Dr. Masgutova received an invitation from Tula State University's post-graduate department to work with children who had been evacuated from the contaminated regions. The displaced children had phobias about atomic war and abandonment. They had diseases that affected their vascular, lymphatic, and respiratory systems, complicating their anxiety and fears. Some children had since been diagnosed with cancer.

Twice per month, Dr. Masgutova collaborated with other psychologists and teachers to help coax children out of post-traumatic stress using different tools, such as movement-based learning, general psychology, and personality development psychology.

She applied concepts of her graduate thesis work in combination with principles of human psychology and psychodynamic, psychomotor, and cognitive psychology approaches—tools she described as "integrative psychophysiological techniques." These recovery tools target the brain's connectivity of the lower brain stem and cortex levels, which are responsible for regulating automaticity and higher-level thinking, motor control, and sensation.

The Chernobyl disaster survivors demonstrated emotional states similar to the kinds of grief and pain that people experience when facing their own mortality.

Dr. Masgutova created an acute and post-trauma recovery program with psychological tools and active movements that helps people progress through seven stages of grief and emotional recovery:

Shock and Denial
Pain and Guilt
Anger and Bargaining
Depression and Loneliness
Reflection and Upward Turn
Reconstruction and Working Through
Acceptance and Hope[57]

This work was influenced by Freud's concepts of personality and structured unconsciousness in trauma and Dr. Elisabeth Kubler-Ross, a Swiss American psychiatrist who penned the book *On Death and Dying*. This groundbreaking twentieth-century book described life, death, transition, and the five stages of grief: (1) denial, (2) anger, (3) bargaining, (4) depression, and (5) acceptance.

The work corresponded to each phase of living through a trauma like Chernobyl, and redirected any feelings of chronic despair into a future of new possibilities, where loss or death was not their destiny.[58]

Dr. Masgutova arrived in Ufa on June 5, one day after the calamity occurred. She immediately began assessing the surviving children. Their reactions and behaviors varied, but the child survivors of the train accident near Ufa shared a common characteristic: they all were in an extreme state of acute stress and severe injury.

The physical manifestations of their trauma were evident. Their breathing was shallow, as if their lungs were safeguarding any available air from within, permitting only that which was necessary to survive to be exhaled. Some children were hypervigilant, their eyes constantly scanning from right to left. They were nervous, impulsive, or aggressive.

Morphine and other opioids were available, funneled into their little bodies according to the maximum allowable schedule. These interventions were necessary, but Dr. Masgutova knew these prolonged treatments were a detriment to the cerebral cortex and the resilience of their fragile extrapyramidal nervous systems.

She moved from child to child, performing anterior and posterior sweeps of the unbandaged areas between their wrists and elbows and between the knees and ankles. The tactile stroking had a calming effect on her patients. Screams and wails de-escalated into a comfortable silence.

Dr. Masgutova expanded her tactility protocol with demonstrations of some basic movements and brain-building exercises—such as homolateral and midline-crossing movements.

The children were in persistent survival mode. Their reflexes were overloading their brain stems. The resulting chronic muscle tension stressed the central nervous system, and motor coordination within their body plane function deteriorated.[59]

Her exercises stimulated all three planes of the body and the corresponding lower-level (survival and instinctual) and higher-level (cortical and rational) brain functions.

The archetype exercises restored and integrated the patterns and links between the brain stem and cortex, which aided the children in trauma recovery. Reflex reintegration provided the gateway to transition from reaction to action, to bring each child into their present and realize their capability to move forward. The exercises inspired her foundational MNRI Archetype Movement Program.

For the children who couldn't move or whose limbs were missing, Dr. Masgutova invited them to watch her and visualize the body movements. She slowly guided the children through a ballet of homologous, homolateral, and cross-body exercises. She thought of her mother's immaculate and graceful style of movement. "Cha-cha, cha-cha-cha," her mother would sing as her toes lifted her body into various poses that carried her through their home kitchen and the adjoining study.

Reproducing the primary reflex patterns through exploratory movement was a gateway to healing, a path toward repairing the damaged neural pathways between each child's brain and body. Their gaze became less attentive to actions on the periphery and more focused on Dr. Masgutova and their own movements. Doodling and painting the air with invisible rainbows enabled their eyes to release their overprotective posture, creating a more relaxed and centralized visual acuity.

Movement freed the children from the past and released them into a place of balance, presence, stability, and inner safety. Some children actually regained their ability to laugh within five days, but this physiological response was not realized for many others until weeks later.[60]

Still, they cried. They cried for pain and the grief of what was lost—skin, appendages, self-confidence, family members, and the normalcy of childhood. They cried for affection. Many of the children pleaded with the medical and support services staff to be embraced for comfort. Every child in the ward had six caregivers, primarily medical students, who were on call at all times. However, the children's pleas often went unanswered.

Dr. Masgutova's gloved hands delicately connected with each child's non-bandaged skin. She acknowledged their pain.

We are here for you. We care about you.

She spoke to them without words, initiating the skin-to-skin contact by stroking downward on the posterior side of their arms, from elbow to wrist. She carefully rotated to the anterior side of the arm. Repeat.

"No, that's the wrong way. Go up," the child responded.

When she got to the anterior surface of the next child's arm, she was met with the same response.

That's odd, she thought, but she obliged.

Skin is the body's largest organ. Skin creates the boundary between a person's inner physical being and the outside world and plays an important role in the way a child experiences life. The role and intensity of touch affect the development of the connectivity of the hemispheres and cortical functions of the brain, and the diencephalon, midbrain, and brain stem. These children, many of whom were parentless, were in deficit of touch.

"Hug me, please," the children begged.

Instead of touching deeper, she held longer.

Even though the exercises helped move some children forward in their emotional state, the vast majority of approximately one hundred children on Dr. Masgutova's caseload, and elsewhere throughout the hospital's floors, continued to display perplexing behaviors. The only recourse for mitigating these behaviors was heavy doses of medicine.

Dr. Masgutova was conflicted: Each child's primary reflexes appeared to be reactive, based on their extreme emotional and neurophysiological symptoms and responses. These early-stage reflexes were considered to be a primitive function of the nervous system and should be inhibited, or otherwise disappear, after a child's first year of life, according to prevailing neuroscience theories in human development.

Many of the children were hyperventilating because of overexcitation. Their palms were tightly closed. Asking the children to open their palms was not a plausible option. They were under duress and couldn't control their responses. Addressing their consciousness did not work.

Dr. Masgutova knew how to check for proper primary reflex responses according to what she had studied in neurophysiology and psychology books. She gently sculpted the exterior of their hands with loving caresses until her thumbs could maneuver into the center of their palms. She applied long, deep pressure to the center of their palms, and their jaws relaxed. Guttural "Ahhs!" decrescendoed into calmer "Ahhhhhhs."

This is all happening not through words but through touch, she thought.

As it turned out, this sensory stimulus revealed the receptor field for the Babkin Palmomental Reflex. Applying a soft, deep pressure into the center of the palm and inviting the child to breathe out with a relaxed jaw prompted the reintegration of this reactive sensorimotor circuit.

Dr. Masgutova's fingers slid down to the bottom of the children's palms. She tested the Hands Supporting Reflex* pattern by pushing downward on the bottom third of their palms and asked each child to push against her palms as if they were lifting the sky. In ordinary circumstances, this should have been an effortless task to complete, as the reflex was to have "disappeared" by the age of these children, but most of the young survivors could not fulfill the request. Their territorial, self-preservation instincts prevented them from completing the task. She depressed her fingers again and pulled down slightly. They could not straighten their elbows enough to touch the sky. She supported each elbow with her free left elbow, while the fingers of the right hand continued with the rhythmical point activations, to activate the receptor field and remind the body of the proper reflex circuit. *Cha-cha, cha-cha-cha.*

Dr. Masgutova recalled the sensations of her late great-grandfather's techniques as she applied deep circular motions to the connection of each child's shoulder and upper chest to release tension. The children responded positively to the deep touch. They started to speak, talk, and move in a proper way. They processed information and responded to directions. They understood they were now safe.[61]

The body's largest organ was burned, but reflex integration held the key to healing.

Like many of her friends and colleagues at Orekhovo-Zuevo State Educational University, Dr. Masgutova juggled the demands of raising a child, engaging with her close-knit yet geographically distant family, fulfilling the domestic responsibilities of a wife, and building a career and reputation. She was accustomed to turning off her lamp well after the beginning of a new day.

The trauma here took a toll. The sixteen-hour days were

marathons for stamina and the soul. Their profession's ethical standards forbade her and other first responders from crying, and at times Dr. Masgutova's heart felt as if it were made of stone. One tear could send a child back in time. Most psychologists could not sustain the rigor of such consequential expectations and left within days. Dr. Masgutova and one colleague remained to manage the hundred-child caseload.

At the end of each seemingly interminable day in Ufa, hours after Denis and Renat had fallen asleep in their nearby rented apartment, Dr. Masgutova would slip into a market near the corner of Ulitsa Mendeleyeva and Ulitsa Minigali Gubaydullina Streets, a short walk from their apartment. She was not there to buy apples or grapes or cold *okroshka* soup. She was there for the produce scale. At first, the manager was gracious. After a while, she crossed her arms over her chest and glared at Dr. Masgutova, suspicious why this customer was always poking her scale and didn't leave the store with any goods. But the scale held the key to the answer Dr. Masgutova was looking for. She continued pressing the scale with her finger, trying to determine the exact measurement of pressure the children favored.

If she could determine this specific depth of proprioceptive touch, Dr. Masgutova could figure out how to go a bit deeper, to reach the damaged extrapyramidal and pyramidal nervous systems of so many of the affected children. Decoding this specific depth of touch was as much a scientific process as it was intuition.

The sensation of touch depends on how sensory receptors interpret the input. Each receptor appraises the stimulus and transmits the information to neurons that send the information along a specific pathway. Each kind of touch, such as light, deep, itchy, or painful, follows a specific path.

Receptors are stimulated through input that includes light touch, deep pressure, skin and muscle stretching, vibration, or movement. The body has many types of touch receptors, and they are activated in different ways based on whether a touch is light and superficial (on the surface of the skin), subcutaneous (below the skin), or deeper and proprioceptive (within the muscles and joints).

The sensory receptors that she needed to connect with were deep and proprioceptive. Each was located within its own domain throughout the hair follicles, skin, muscles and ligaments, tendons, and joints. Merkel's discs in the skin trigger serotonin release. The Ruffini nerve endings in the epidermis and tendons are aroused by warmth, stretching, pressure, and touch. Meissner's corpuscles huddle beneath the surface of the skin and are stirred by touch and vibration. The Golgi receptors stimulate the processes of posture control and movement and muscle-tone regulation. She needed to reach all these sensory receptors with a specific depth of touch.

After multiple nightly visits to the produce market and cross-checking her estimates against the children's responses, Dr. Masgutova found the answer she was looking for: 360 grams per centimeter squared.

Subsequent years of research and observations would reveal this measurement equates to what the MNRI Method defined as generalized tactility*—or the general perception and sensation by the body. The MNRI Method theorizes this measurement also represents the pressure of the amniotic fluid within which an embryo develops and the depth of a mother's thoracic embrace of her infant as her fingers instinctually cradle the region of the fifth and sixth ribs. The proportional squeeze between the birth canal and the baby's cranial bones and rib cage during the birthing process also approximates to 360 grams per centimeter squared, according to Dr. Masgutova's theory. This intense activation of pressure and the Golgi receptors also switch on the suck, swallow, breathing, and satiation functions once a baby is born.

The movements and tactile and reflex integration techniques in Ufa brought momentary and then prolonged relief to the children. The children began to accept that their tragedy was in the past. Their minds shifted from survival in the moment to an awareness that their tragedy was an event that occurred on June 4, 1989, a finite date on the continuum of time. Movement-oriented therapy and touch enabled each hemisphere of the brain to reestablish communication within itself as negative anchors associated with vulnerability were released. When brain activity flowed interdependently and simultaneously within the left and right hemispheres, a foundation for future-integrated communication in the cortex occurred. The brain interpreted objectively.[62]

The impact of the movement-oriented therapy and tactility treatment spread throughout the hospital. Morphine doses were reduced. In fewer than three weeks, the death rate decreased in the wards in which Dr. Masgutova's movement-oriented therapy and reflex integration had been implemented.

The days and months spun in all directions, like a compass in an electromagnetic field. The children's physiological and psychological states improved, and for that Dr. Masgutova was grateful.

However, there were many times when an incidental error sent a breakthrough on a collision course with relapse.

Psychiatrists had reduced one child's medication levels due to his medical and emotional progress. One day, without warning, guttural screams erupted from his body, and a tranquilizer was immediately administered. The child tore off his shirt and ripped the sleeve of the uniform of a nearby nurse, who had commanded him earlier that day to clean up some juice he had spilled on the floor. Dr. Masgutova rushed in as the medicine anesthetized his screams and she pulled him toward his bed.

"What happened? Why is he screaming?"

Dr. Masgutova took a deep breath and reoriented her energy. The boy's arms became increasingly clumsy as the morphine's effects took hold.

"I want to die. I want to die. I want to die," he whispered.

A roommate leaned over his bed and whispered into her ear.

"He just found out his parents died in the train accident," the child said.

The boy didn't think he had anyone who loved him. He had reacted out of fear, terrified he would never leave the hospital again. He tucked his head into his knees, and it seemed as if he were holding his breath, immobilized because of this newfound stress.

Dr. Masgutova cried for him through hours of the Embrace Squeeze technique. She notated that he was psychologically stable and did not need further medicating drugs in his chart. But the next evening, she walked into his room to find him in a state of stupor. A storm had blown up inside, and Dr. Masgutova's tears threatened to break loose. With gale-force determination, she invaded the psychiatrist's personal space.

"What happened? Why is he in this state? Please do not go near this child again," she demanded.

The psychiatrist had not meant intentional harm, nor was he being neglectful. In these situations, indifference was impossible. He had followed protocol without considering the evaluation of progress that she and the medical doctors had notated.

Another child screamed at his nurse to bring him a mirror, because his parents had just seen him for the first time. His bandaged face and the gap where his nose had been had frightened them. The child drew a picture of a face covered with lines, with one eye, no nose, big ears, and fangs from the mouth.

"This is the devil with one eye. This is me," he said.

After that, visitors and caregivers were forbidden to bring any kind of reflective object into the hospital that could show a child their reflection. All mirrors were removed from the walls.

Each day of survival required herculean efforts for the children. The medication may have saved them, but it was also slowly poisoning their nervous systems. One ten-year-old boy and his sister struggled to survive for twenty days. The boy's kidneys began to shut down as a result of a cocktail of painkillers. His physiological state worsened, and he ended up in the emergency room with kidney failure.

Shock can be lethal if the body is not freed from its immobile state. The children on Dr. Masgutova's caseload had emerged out of shock within the first couple of days, while the children who were not part of the movement-oriented therapy and reflex integration techniques remained in a prolonged state of shock.

Exiting the ward was like walking death row. The reams of paper were now hospital wallpaper, the names of the deceased children—now one out of every six—creating a helter-skelter pattern of sorrow.

It was usually after midnight by the time Dr. Masgutova returned to their rented Ufa apartment. Most nights, Denis slept peacefully. She gently maneuvered him into the center of their bed. Renat was usually asleep. She lay down and moved close to Denis so that their faces were almost touching, like two halves of one heart.

Dr. Masgutova thought of her life in Ufa six years before, when she gave birth to the boy who was now nearly half as tall as she. She had bookended her days of lecturing with forty-five-minute sessions of medical training, twice a day, five days a week, to help improve her body's potential for a successful pregnancy.

Once, a senior department colleague invited her into his office and remarked that she was not meant to have a child.

"You are exhausting yourself. Perhaps we can have you talk with one of your colleagues if you need additional counseling," he said.

The psychologist's estimation was, in fact, wrong, as she soon discovered when her doctor gifted her with the news that she was four weeks pregnant.

She knew it was meant to be.

She refused the epidural in favor of a natural birth.

She held Denis for the first time.

The doctor wanted to give her a nutrient, a hormone and protein booster in the form of blood plasma, which she refused. It was protocol, he insisted. She relented. Her blood pressure soared. Her newborn baby, Denis, was taken as a team of specialists surged in. Other nursing mothers breastfed Denis over the next few days.

She lost a lot of blood, and then she lost consciousness.

There was warmth and radiant light.

Now, six years later, Dr. Masgutova was back at the hospital in Ufa. She saw her precious Denis for brief moments each day during her breaks from volunteering with the children. They crunched on apple slices and nibbled on plain pieces of bread. Denis, Renat, and Dr. Masgutova played hide-and-seek in the communal picnic area outside. Another victim of the railway disaster, whose name was also Denis, eventually joined them. He had curly, wiry red hair. He was twelve years old. Denis spent many days alone in the hospital. The clinic had been unable to locate his family. Dr. Masgutova began to think he had no one in his life who loved him and would come for him when he was considered well enough to be discharged.

In this precarious state, they could not leave him behind.

Dr. Masgutova initiated plans to adopt him. Her father prepared the paperwork.

Toward the end of her four months of volunteering, and one day prior to Denis's official adoption, the Ufa hospital experienced another breakthrough. Staff members connected with Denis's uncle. Dr. Masgutova, Renat, and their Denis parted ways with the nearly adopted boy.

After dedicating more than eighteen hundred volunteer hours to save the lives of so many young ones, Dr. Masgutova never saw the children again. They were injured birds who eventually flew away.

As the train oscillated on Dr. Masgutova's solo journey back to Moscow, she considered her own values and what they foretold of tomorrow and beyond. She had a promising academic career in a country on the precipice of a brighter future. She was caught in a quagmire, perplexed about whether traditional theories of reflex inhibition were neurodevelopmentally appropriate. There were too many questions, and those questions had to be answered.

Certain traditional theories considered reflexes to be primitive responses that become cortically inhibited with normal development, while others saw reflexes as primary responses that become integrated. She was conflicted with the prevailing concepts of reflex inhibition versus reflex maturation. Why must primary reflexes be considered "primitive" and needing to be extinguished if still active beyond a certain developmental life stage?

Per Sechenov, excitation and inhibition are two sides of the central nervous system process, and they must work in balance. The inhibitory process was a natural course of central nervous system development and established the roles of reflex responses and consciously controlled actions.

Did this process require the full neurological maturation/myelination of reflex circuit nerve pathways? What happened to this process if a reflex was retained or became reactive due to a traumatic event? Must this reactivity be stopped with external inhibiting procedures instead of helping the reflex to mature or reintegrate neurologically? What would happen with the protection task of a reflex that was inhibited? Were there more logical and practical approaches than inhibition?

Was a reflex genetic or socially automatic? Could a reflex pattern be remodulated?

A true, sympathetic deep touch was the tool for releasing a person from intermittent, prolonged, and chronic stress after a traumatic event. But what were the technical constructs of this touch? If a reflexive response was triggered, did that mean the pathology had been reinforced, or had she discovered a novel modality that could help children and adults affected by trauma?

Life in the Soviet Union had changed, and so had she. It was a time of endings and new beginnings. This was the time of perestroika and glasnost, when the communist stranglehold over information and other systems was weakening. Gorbachev was about to declare the Soviet Academy of Sciences a self-governing organization, releasing it from the tentacles of government control. The promise of new freedoms was rising on the horizon, like sunrays pushing the cloak of hulking, steel-gray clouds out of the way.

The protests in Tiananmen Square earlier in 1989 had failed to incite major political change in China, but the parliamentary elections in Poland on June 4, 1989, triggered the peaceful fall of Polish communism. Hungary raised its portion of the so-called Iron Curtain, and it seemed the Soviet Union was headed that way as well. For much of the twentieth century, religious worship had been strictly restricted, and religious persecution had intensified during Svetlana's childhood in the 1960s, with more churches closed under Khrushchev than under Stalin. Those who defied the laws of the land and conducted prayer meetings or baptisms in secret subjected themselves to potential prison sentences if they were caught by the undercover KGB officers monitoring "anti-Soviet" behavior. That was changing. The freedom to worship more openly had spread. Dr. Masgutova said prayers to herself, and sometimes she mouthed them aloud, wondering if the universal God could now hear her better.

The smell of death, the shrieks and wails, the stricken faces—all felt as if they were invading each hemisphere of her brain. Her temples felt as if they were constantly absorbing the strikes. She walked to work instead of taking the train, but the crowded streets of Moscow teemed with smokers. Each flicker of a match sparked memories of the past four months, and she felt like she was caught in one of Dante's concentric circles of hell. She recited poems to distract her thinking.

Dr. Masgutova thought of Anna Akhmatova, one of her favorite poets, who frequently entertained cabaret crowds with her incendiary lyrical poetry readings during Russia's prerevolutionary period. Anna had encountered her own form of repression, having eventually been denounced as an ideological adversary, and by 1925, her publications had been officially suppressed.

During the years of Stalin's reign, she composed little, though took great risks between the years of 1935 and 1940 to pen her long narrative poem, *Rekviem* ("Requiem"), a tribute to the victims of terror. If caught by the secret police, she could've been jailed. The poem was published for the first time in 1989, in the journal *Oktiabr'* ("October"). The poem survived because Anna whispered different lines to her closest friends, who committed them to memory. The smoldering remnants of smoked cigarettes lapped away at the scraps of paper upon which she wrote her lines, until they disintegrated from embers into ashtray dust.

No, neither under an alien sky nor
Under the protection of alien wings
I remained with my own people then,
Where my people, in their misfortune, were.[63]

I could hear the remaining participants of the MNRI Post-Trauma Recovery Conference laughing in the lobby on the other side of the building. Their light chatter quieted as the last few individuals departed.

The wall clock ticked.

Several moments passed before Dr. Masgutova concluded her final reflections on her post-trauma recovery work in Ufa.

"I remember one parent asked me if it were better if their child were dead than to go through life without a nose," Dr. Masgutova recalled. "Mothers and fathers of the child survivors had transferred fears to their children. At that time, I wondered where the boundary lay between the soul and the mind. The biggest gift in this world is life. Nobody has the right to take away life, or make any kind of decision like that, except for the universal God.

"Those first few days after I returned to Moscow, I was sleeping only four hours, and that was what I was used to, because I was young. But the images were overwhelming, and when the whole catastrophe was finished, I was walking to work instead of taking the bus. It was about an hour's walk, and I was walking to release stress," she recalled. "All I saw were faces, faces, faces. There was a bridge over the trains, and I knew the exact time the trains would pass. It took the train seven minutes to pass through the station. My songs stopped. My poems stopped. When those trains passed me below, I screamed as loud as I could—*Ahhhhhhh! Ahhhhhhh! Ahhhhhhh!*—to try and let go of the images.

"Children were dying in our hands, and as first responders, we had no help from others. We were not allowed to cry. I was supposed to be an iron psychologist, but I am human at the same time."

CHAPTER 7

Degrees of Freedom

Soviet neurophysiologist Nikolai Alexandrovich Bernstein (1896–1966) pioneered discoveries in the biomechanics of human movements and movement control by analyzing people performing everyday actions such as eating with a spoon, pounding a nail with a hammer, or playing the piano. He compared normal and deviated gait patterns in children, adults, the elderly, and neurologic patients. He spent months drawing charts and poring over calculations of velocities, accelerations, and muscle torques in each joint of a body in motion on the basis of spatial coordinates with joints.[64]

Bernstein's exertions prompted him to propose a theory of hierarchal control of action and movement coordination. Movement coordination centered around a concept of "degrees of freedom," he determined. In its most basic sense, the concept asserts that there are multiple ways for humans to perform a movement to achieve the same goal, eliciting the question of how the brain chooses a course of action among infinite ones.[65]

His studies of human movement, both in neurotypical populations and in individuals with brain damage, led to considerable advancements in motor learning and models for stages of learning—not only in intellectual and emotional development but also movement development.

The human body has 244 degrees of freedom, controlled by 630 muscles. There are about 230 joints in the body, most of which have one degree of freedom, although some joints, such as the hip and the shoulder, can have multiple. Just how the central nervous system is capable of controlling the many degrees of freedom of the musculoskeletal system still vexes modern scientists.[66]

The body's basic freedom of movement in three-dimensional space is controlled by three axes that permit the body to move in six different directions—linearly (front to back, up and down, and left to right) and rotationally (often referred to as pitch, roll, and yaw). Most of the body's movements are voluntary and controlled by higher-level functions of the brain.

The human hand alone has twenty-seven degrees of freedom: four in each finger (three for flexion and extension, one for abduction and adduction), five in the thumb, and six degrees of freedom for rotation and translation of the wrist.[67]

It is said that the human hand is one of the most extraordinary parts of the entire human body. The hand's complicated anatomy and its composition of an advanced muscular system and ligaments reveal it to be a complex manipulator, a biomechanical feat of genetic engineering enabling a person to accomplish both gross and fine motor skills, to self-sustain, explore, protect, guide, feel, and touch.[68]

Dr. Masgutova's hands have inadvertently excavated the truths of betrayal and indiscretion. She has absorbed the stories of people who are encumbered with their own lives or have been abused. Her hands have rehabilitated children and adults who have survived natural and man-made disasters, women who have been tortured, children who have witnessed their elders being burned during war, little ones who had been locked in a cabinet at gunpoint, victims of sexual abuse, and mothers and fathers who have carried the trauma of unexpectedly losing their children through manifestations of physical conditions.

The depths of life's traumas and recovery are contoured into Dr. Masgutova's hands, as the selected anonymous testimonials that follow aim to reveal.

▲

I experienced a bad fall while attending a family conference overseas. I wondered if I had broken my neck. I could not move and felt like I was floating.

Svetlana and Denis were nearby and ran over. They immediately began restoring my breathing reflexes, and other reflexes, pulling me back into my body. Svetlana helped me stand up, and she then guided me toward a treatment table. They applied NeuroStructural Reflex Integration and other techniques on specific areas of my body that regulate the HPA stress axis and reduce the flow of stress hormones. They reintegrated reflexes such as the Trunk Extension and Tonic Labyrinthine. Svetlana helped me to stand up again and invited me to start walking.

Her hands were like X-rays. I heard the clicks of her Kissing Stars as she realigned eight vertebrae to protect my neck. We went to the hospital, and she described in a foreign language the fall and subsequent intervention with the doctors. They took X-rays and confirmed nothing was broken. They sent me home with over-the-counter pain medication. I had no pain at all. My husband is a medical doctor, and he assured me that had it not been for Denis and Svetlana, I would have been in the hospital for days, with occupational therapy for months.

▲

My youngest sister was found lifeless in her apartment. Her heart had inexplicably stopped beating. During the few weeks following her death, I remained in an extreme state of denial, anger, and persistent confusion. I discovered a whole new level of pain and an unimaginable depth of sadness. My family has always been everything to me, and we all instantly became the reason for each other to survive the excruciating reality.

From the moment I shared my tragedy with Svetlana, she was present for me. In her very first message filled with strong support and love, she wrote, "You have only one choice—to be strong and to let go."

How could I have dismissed her advice knowing that she understood the feeling of losing a younger sister? Her professional and personal experiences had already made a positive impact on my distressed state.

About three weeks after the funeral, Svetlana invited me to take part in a post-trauma recovery session. I remember the warmth of her hands and her therapeutic touch in the healing process. I remember being overwhelmed by her generosity in sharing her personal searching journey for her own sister's soul. Despite the multiple tragedies and challenging events that shook her own life, she continues to demonstrate this strong desire to change the world to be a better and more caring place.

▲

The work you have created is a heaven-sent gift to all who suffer, and I am so grateful for the sacrifices you make to bring this method to the broken and hurting souls around the world like me. What I want to tell you is that I am a soul that you are painting a new picture for with the work you do, and part of my body is coming back to life.

▲

Svetlana and I first met in Moscow in 1991, when my husband and I worked for one year as Rotary International volunteers at Russia's Open University. Later, Svetlana and I found out we both were part of the crowd who witnessed the events around the 1991 Soviet coup d'état attempt, or August Coup—the detainment and attempted removal of Mikhail Gorbachev. We watched as the tanks rolled down the street as they tried to take over the White House. Both Svetlana and I were aware of the role of the babushkas as those grandmothers formed a line across the street and stopped the tanks. I later found out Svetlana was hand in hand with the babushkas.

After the unsuccessful coup, our work at the university continued. She was very helpful in my understanding of Ivan M. Sechenov and his role in reflex development within primary motor movements, which I included in my doctoral dissertation.

In 2003, when I found out she was teaching Dynamic and Postural Reflex Integration, I knew I wanted to learn more about her work in this area. I signed up for the class.

Unfortunately, within the first few hours of the class, I began to feel intense pain in my lower back that I had never experienced before. So rather than leaving the class, she suggested I wait for the break when she and her son, Denis, could work on my back to relieve the pain.

They worked on my lower spine using reflex integration methods involving post-trauma and NeuroStructural techniques. Everything broke loose emotionally when they hit the point on L4 and L5. Despite my concern that many in the class were standing around the table to watch them work, I had no control over the anger, which caused me to cry and pound the table using curse words I did not know I knew.

Finally, a shudder went through my body, and I realized I had no control over the death of my son, who had been hit by a truck and killed while riding his bicycle to a graduation party for his master's degree in counseling.

After a few hours, when the work had integrated into my body, I returned to class without experiencing any pain. The grief I had harbored in my body resulted in recurring bladder cancer five times. Because of the work done that day, I haven't had bladder cancer again.

▲

Dr. Masgutova's decision to focus on the role of primary reflexes in human development occurred during one of the most pivotal times in her country's history. The Union of the Soviet Socialist Republics was on the cusp of the fall of communism, foretelling the possibilities of openness and freedom, of hope and new opportunities.

Upon her return to Moscow after her Ufa volunteer work, Dr. Masgutova rejoined her university posts. She lectured on and published articles about the attitudes of teachers and parents toward teenagers' emotions. This was an emotionally volatile time. Dr. Masgutova struggled with the traumatic railway experience and the destinies of the lives she and other first responders had saved—faces that lived on in her memory but that she would never see again. It seemed to her as if the people of Moscow had not even realized the railway disaster had happened, at least not publicly. Much like the Chernobyl disaster, acknowledgments of human responsibility in man-made catastrophes were not suitable in the public forum.

Privately, her colleagues felt otherwise. They implored her to be candid about her experiences rehabilitating the children. She authored educational and journal articles about the application of her method of active work and psychological rehabilitation to children in extreme events.[69] She summarized the content of the publications but avoided relaying the agony the children had lived through.

Flashbacks of the children's tragedies replayed in her consciousness.

Where are they now? How much pain are they still in? Did I do enough? Why did this have to happen to them? What happened to Denis, my almost-adopted child? Is he okay? Does he think about us? Will I ever see any of those children again?

She willed silence to suppress her stream of consciousness.

The year before, Dr. Masgutova had founded a private educational institute for psychological assistance for children and adults. Her clients were children diagnosed with schizophrenia or cancer or who were dependent on post-surgery narcotics, and adults who were depressed or suicidal. This practical work informed her published research on teenage psychology. During nonclinical hours, the institute was an incubator, a lab for experimenting with the concept of "remodulating" nine primary reflex patterns.[70]

She continued her experiential work at home with Renat and nine-year-old Denis.

Remodulating reflex patterns required a precise understanding of the body's sensory receptor fields and the specific depth of touch that would elicit the appropriate response to a stimulus. This process also required knowledge about motion in reflex reactions and about the latency and intensity of a response after a stimulus.

Is the sensory stimulus leading to the correct response or sequence of responses? Does the strength of the response reflect the intensity of the input? Is the reflex response occurring immediately after the stimulus is elicited, or is there a delay? Is the symmetry of response apparent in the body structure, the reflex motion, response time, and intensity of the reaction?

A single blink of the eye corresponds to the speed at which a nerve impulse travels along a neural pathway, or nerve conduction velocity. The average reaction time for a visual stimulus is one-fourth of a second, 0.17 seconds for an audio stimulus, and 0.15 seconds for a tactile stimulus. The diameter of the nerve and the amount of myelination affect nerve conduction velocity. The electrical signaling in the human body's nervous system travels at 150 miles per hour, so pinpointing deviations in the quality of a response was critical to understanding how to repattern a reflex.

Three to five exercise repetitions could repattern the reflex. Other times, results were accomplished in days, weeks, or even months.

Dr. Masgutova spent the following years conducting clinical testing and real-time trauma recovery work to develop exercises that could reintegrate the primary infant reflexes that had resurfaced under stress. Developing these techniques required a precise comprehension of the complex neurosensorimotor circuitry of each of the genetically encoded primary reflex patterns.

These reflex integration techniques were unavailable to body-oriented practitioners and pediatricians. They would not have been useful to mainstream doctors and psychologists because, according to prevailing theory, reminding the body of so-called inhibited reflex patterns could reinforce the pathology of the reflex.

Dr. Masgutova's eponymous reflex integration method evolved as the weakening of the central government and the indications of the collapse of the USSR reverberated in different ways throughout the country and its republics. Geopolitical tensions and natural disasters unraveled the sociocultural stitches of societies. Trauma recovery continued to shape the direction of her work, nearby and far.

Then, massive waves of violence in the Azerbaijani capital

of Baku forced thousands of ethnic Armenians to leave their homes. By January 1990, a seven-day pogrom, also known as Black January, broke out against the Armenian inhabitants of Baku. Armenians were brutally beaten and killed.[71] A crowd of Armenians and Russians who were in Baku fled and registered at an emergency center in Moscow.

Dr. Masgutova and her colleagues volunteered to treat the post-traumatic disorders of fourteen of the Black January internally displaced people.[72] The survivors of the Baku conflict were in devastating states of acute stress. They demonstrated many behaviors similar to those of the children who were victims of the Ufa railway catastrophe.

The stress state of a ten-year-old boy was especially severe. His hair was the color of ash, and he stuttered as he tried to articulate what he had just been through.

The boy had fled with his mother, who also was being treated at the emergency center. It took them two days, fighting destruction and death, before they reached an airport that could provide safe transportation to Moscow. He and his mother had witnessed their neighbor, a retired army officer, being beaten with a metal pipe and left for dead in a pile of garbage and other bodies. During this conflict, the weapons for human massacres were mostly knives and rocks, intended to inflict the most painful deaths.

The topic of memory erasure, or the selective artificial removal of memories or associations, was brought up during interdisciplinary team discussions about how to help the children cope with their trauma.

But Dr. Masgutova was opposed, arguing that memory erasure cuts the level of consciousness. Further, the Fear Paralysis response, which is genetically designed to handle stress, wouldn't work properly if any such technique were to be applied.

A blend of educational kinesiology, NeuroTactile, and

NeuroStructural therapies and reflex repatterning exercises were incorporated into her team's treatment plans for the evacuees, including the ten-year-old boy. He flinched and withdrew in tactile defense. In those initial days of therapy, the only touch his body accepted was Dr. Masgutova's Embrace Squeeze. She spent hours on this single technique, folding and cupping her hands and gently applying even pressure over his forearms and lower legs.

"We care about you. You are brave and strong. You are a winner," she said.

Initially, Dr. Masgutova held each position for about five seconds to encourage the transmission of the electrical conductivity between the muscle fibers and the brain, per Bernstein's ideas surrounding biomechanics and the physiology of movement. She discovered that if she held each position longer, the electrical conductivity between the skin, muscles, tendons, and bones was more effective and lasting.

Dr. Masgutova's post-trauma recovery work with the Baku conflict survivors revealed key distinctions between the Moro* (fight-and-flight) and Fear Paralysis* (startle) responses, which, until that time, had been considered to be under the domain of a single reflex (usually referred to as "withdrawal" or "startle"). The hyperactivity of these two separate protective reflex patterns was evident in the children and required definitive approaches to restore the integrity of each reflex circuit.

Ernst Moro[73] first described the Moro reflex in 1918 at a lecture for the Society of Natural History and Medicine in Heidelberg. He had observed some peculiar motor reactions in infants during their first three months of life. When he placed an infant on a pillow on an examination table and tapped his hands on both sides of the pillow, the infant's arms extended symmetrically, then folded into each other with a slight tremor in movement.

The Moro Embrace Reflex Pattern was elicited by a sudden

head position change or sudden stability loss. Activation of the Moro response triggered the limbs to move from core to periphery, followed by periphery to core. This reflex pattern became reactive when the victims of the Baku conflict needed to curl up into a ball to protect themselves from brutality or to prevent themselves from falling while fleeing from violence.

On the other hand, the Fear Paralysis Reflex Pattern was elicited by a sudden and intense tactile, auditory, or visual stimulation. Activation of Fear Paralysis elicited a strong sympathetic response, followed immediately by a parasympathetic response to freeze the body. Witnessing violence and death activated the Fear Paralysis pattern.

The excessive fear reactions—the phobias, anxiety, fatigue, disassociation, and avoidance behaviors—signaled that these hyperactive responses had remained active, damaging their nervous systems and anchoring the children to their traumas. The Moro and Fear Paralysis Reflex Patterns (and the Tendon Guard Reflex Pattern) were genetically designed to handle stress and were the most susceptible to damage if stress became too intense or prolonged.[74]

Dr. Masgutova's tactile stroking awakened the body, which released the child from the shock of stress and helped restore a feeling of safety. To reintegrate the Fear Paralysis Reflex Pattern, she tapped on the sensory receptive fields on each child's sternum and then on the biomechanical sensory gravity points on the bottom of the feet to activate balance and shock absorption.[75] The chest tapping penetrated the nerve plexus that controlled cardiac function and the thymus gland to help regulate heartbeat and immunity. The tapping on the foot's biomechanical sensory points transmitted sensory input to the cranial nerves, including the vagus nerve, or the tenth cranial nerve, which interfaced with the parasympathetic control of the heart, lungs, and digestive tract. The tapping calmed down the intense sympathetic response.

Cha-cha, cha-cha-cha.

The gentle tapping was applied three to seven times per child, with pauses between each exercise to enable neurological integration. This exercise was performed only twice per week.

The sensory activation of the Moro reflex began with an invitation for the child to carefully bring their chin forward and up, tilting their head thirty degrees backward. She applied a microstretch to the neck muscles. Dr. Masgutova initiated the reflex pattern's motor activation by inviting each child to cross their arms and bring their knees up into their chest, as if they were rolling up into a ball. Then the child slowly extended their limbs and tilted their head and chin back, angled upward. The second stage of this repatterning exercise involved a cross-lateral activation of the reflex pattern that invited the child to experience the inward protective movement of the reflex. Each child lay on their back and brought the opposite knee and elbow together in maximum flexion, and then extended the opposite limbs partially apart. The children were encouraged to hug teddy bears that were provided in order to integrate the final Moro stage 3 and initiate bonding, beginning with the comfort of the teddy bear.

The reintegration of each reflex pattern helped free the reflex from its rigid automatic responses and impulsivity. Reintegration also released fear and anxiety through the thalamus, amygdala, and insula.

The ash-haired child's normal black hair color returned within days, and his stuttering eased into coherent language.[76]

Dr. Masgutova recognized that the children could have been swallowed by their past and excitation had they started talking about what they had seen. They suffered internally, but their subconscious wanted to move forward. This concept of revictimization was prohibited in her body-oriented post-trauma recovery work.

"We should not come to this world to suffer," she said to the child. "Our tragic pasts are not worthy to spoil our today and our future. Do you agree?"

The boy nodded. "Yes, I agree."

"What is your name? What is your age today? What are your future goals? Who are you in your future? Look ahead to the horizon, which is a magnet for your future," she said to him. "Let's set the positive perspective and walk toward your goals."

Dr. Masgutova's work in Ufa as well as her continued clinical work and neurophysiological research revealed more answers to her questions about the role of reflex schemes as a support of neurodevelopment.

Dr. Masgutova and her team overshadowed the visible and invisible scars inflicted by the darkness of humanity. They were not immune from their own psychological trauma due to working with the evacuees. The absorption of pain from each fragile body had to be exchanged with customized exercise protocols that targeted their own associated feelings of stress. Each session was highly personal, an exchange of recovery with a person's psychological trauma.

Dr. Masgutova formulated exercises to model reflex patterns so that she and her colleagues remained "integrated" throughout their trauma recovery work. The protocols included breathing exercises, self-centering techniques, and movements to manage incoming stress and support their central nervous and immune systems. Integration and full presence bridged the effectiveness of the work, of the specialist being able to expertly provide so that the traumatized person can receive the work. Displays of vulnerability from the workers could have been detrimental to results and the impacted individual's health.

Emotional release was permissible only beyond the borders of the psychological assistance center. Dr. Masgutova encouraged her colleagues to feel empathy and sympathy, but of course tears were forbidden during work.

"You are human, and you can cry," she said to her colleagues. "But never cry in the presence of the child or adult who is receiving your work. You must stay positive and strong. They will feel this and will be open to new levels of emotional recovery."

However, the experience of holding children on the precipice of life and death left an indelible mark, and Dr. Masgutova began to question the principles and humanity of this professional code of ethics. She wanted to treat through connection and empathy. After she encountered excruciating loss, she would change her viewpoint, and indeed, only when the circumstance was appropriate, would she cry with a client after completing a trauma recovery session.

IN THEIR WORDS

Helen Kimovna, Dr. Masgutova's Late Sister
Moscow, 1991

Положи меня на ладошку
И укрой своей тёплой рукой
Put me on your palm
And cover me with your warm hand

Отпусти на прямую дорожку
От беды и обиды укрой,
Let me go on a straight path
Hide me from misfortune and anguish

Душу добром наполни,

Звёздной водой окропи
Удача и счастье запомни, у нас впереди.
Fill my heart with Goodness
Sprinkle starry water
Remember the luck and happiness we have
ahead.

Пушистое облако вдохнёт в нас силу
A fluffy cloud will breathe its power into us

Дождь смелости нам придаст
The rain will give us courage

Жизнь даст Солнце—Явило . . .
Счастье и радость будут у нас
Life will give the Sun—Revealed
And Happiness and Joy will be with us

CHAPTER 8

On Your Palm

FLORIDA, February 2020—The room was a mix of special-occasion wear, professional attire, and military dress. About 120 people representing thirty-four countries were gathered at the US Citizenship and Immigration Services Orlando Field Office to become naturalized citizens of the United States of America. These individuals had waited years, even decades, for this milestone.

Dr. Masgutova had anticipated this moment since her first visit to the United States in 1994, shortly after a devastating family tragedy. She felt the presence of her late youngest sister, Helen, during this significant life event.

The citizens-to-be were seated within several rows in the center of the room. Loved ones surrounded them on each side and along the back wall. Dr. Masgutova's grandson, Janek, was seated in the front row along one of the sides, not far from where she stood. He leaned forward. His blue eyes were wide and excited. His smartphone camera was poised.

"Babcia! Babcia!"

She placed her certificate of naturalization over her heart. His phone captured several historical moments.

Janek of Poland was not yet a teen, but he already had demonstrated a keen interest in the MNRI Method and had developed some of his own techniques. Janek was adept in karate, football, geography, world history, and languages (Polish, English, Russian, and Spanish). He also grew up around MNRI, studying alongside his mother, Ela, who has served as vice director of the Międzynarodowy Instytut dr Swietłany Masgutowej (International Dr. Svetlana Masgutova Institute) in Poland.

Dr. Masgutova and the newly christened naturalized citizens of the United States of America rose when their country of origin was named.

She placed her palm over her heart and recited the Pledge of Allegiance in unison with all the other citizens. The lights dimmed, and a white projection screen displayed a series of images from the nation's past that represented the essence of America—a country of immigrants, a nation enriched with different traditions, belief systems, food, identity, language, culture, and history.

Beside an image of the Statue of Liberty was an excerpt from "The New Colossus," written in 1883 by Emma Lazarus as a way to finance the construction of the statue's pedestal.

> *Give me your tired, your poor, your huddled masses yearning to breathe free.*

Then:

> *Even though you become a United States citizen today, you retain your country's traditions and culture, your unique cuisine, your*

beautiful art, music, and literature. It is your obligation to teach your children about their heritage. That is what the United States is all about. A union of immigrant cultures from all over the world.

At the end of the ceremony, the event's presider asked each person to officialize their citizenship by signing their naturalization certificate.

"You have just participated in the history of the United States," he said. "I hope you will take this afternoon to celebrate with loved ones and friends. Who here will be going back to work or serving their country?"

Dr. Masgutova raised her hand with other new citizens of the United States.

She was ready to return to work serving humanity.

By early evening, Dr. Masgutova, now a US citizen, was seated in her living room, beneath the gallery of family portraits, looking up at the black-and-white portrait of Helen, which hung above a framed photo of Dr. Masgutova and baby Janek. Long dark curls cascaded down the sides of Helen's face.

She wore a ruffled white blouse laced with sunflowers. Helen's expression appeared as if she were midway through a shared laugh with the photographer.

"Helen lived and died in every moment," Dr. Masgutova said. "She felt each experience, each emotion, so deeply. She expressed herself through her work with children. Today was for Helen."

Helen was creative, theatrical, and whimsical. She was the center of attention, either in local community theater performances or during poetry recitations for family and neighbor gatherings. She left behind more than three hundred poems, compiled into a book that remains in the family home in Kirgiz-Miyaki.

Helen was born when Svetlana was fifteen years old and about to leave Kirgiz-Miyaki to attend university in Ufa. Svetlana checked in with her family two times per week by visiting a local telephone station not far from the Bashkir State Pedagogical University. She typically only saw her family, including her new baby sister, once a month. They had a relationship that was more akin to that of a mother and daughter, given the age gap.

"She was fiercely independent and courageous from a young age," Dr. Masgutova recalled. "She was a talented singer. Even though she could not roll her *r*'s at the age of four, this did not deter her from singing onstage."

Like her oldest sister, Helen chose to pursue a career in psychology. She moved in with Dr. Masgutova, Renat, and Denis while attending university in Moscow.

"Denis and Helen had the relationship of a brother and sister. Children at our psychological center loved her crazily," Dr. Masgutova said. "Children would ask her to attend their weekend birthday parties, and she always made a promise to go. I told her she needed to work seriously. Helen always stayed true to her promise and her heart."

One day, while entering Dr. Masgutova's apartment, Helen was shot several times by a gunman. A friend found her on the floor. The bullets had entered through her nose and were lodged in the kidney, heart, pericardium, and cervical area, causing the blood to pool from within the body. Her friend called the paramedics, and the rescue squad transported Helen by ambulance to the nearest hospital. The presiding surgeon did not immediately admit her. Helen battled for her life in the waiting room for as long as her body would physically permit.

"I eventually went to the police station. I wanted the records. I wanted to know who did this to her. The police would not cooperate. These were not easy times. There were a lot of random shootings and criminal behavior by bandits. I don't think they even had all the records.

"I went to the hospital. I confronted the surgeon, and I demanded he look me in the eyes, but he could not. He begged me not to pursue the case, because he had two children and could face legal consequences if negligence was proven. I told him I had words to say. Again, I demanded he look me in the eyes."

I forgive you. I am letting go.

"He still would not look me in the eyes."

In her living room, Dr. Masgutova retrieved her computer from the nearby glass table and lifted the screen. She glided her cursor to the upper-right corner of the frame and selected a single document titled "Dear Helen," written in 1994.

It was the last day of May in Moscow. The trees and flowers were blossoming. I arrived home after a full day of lecturing at the university. The world felt so perfect and so beautiful.

I entered through the door of my apartment. Renat was there, and he was in tears. This was the first time I had seen him cry.

"Svetlana, Helen was killed. She was shot several hours ago."

His words hurt my ears and pierced my stomach.

I asked if he was crazy. There was no reason to shoot a twenty-year-old girl—lovely, beautiful, and who cared for children so deeply. She was so amazingly talented in so many ways.

His words were the biggest, darkest storm thundering through my mind. I couldn't even define my level of confusion. It was too much for a human to be able to stand. There really was no reason to shoot people, especially young ones. She was just beginning her life. My head was breaking apart. My heart was burning. I tried to squeeze it to keep it in place.

"It is a mistake," I said.

I became angry and defiant.

"You are wrong," I informed him.

"No, Svetlana, it is not a mistake," he replied. "You need to go to the morgue to identify her."

I went into conflict with my husband.

"I will find her myself," I said.

Any information I heard further on I denied completely.

My husband drove me to the hospital, and there I saw her. My dearest sister who was like my daughter. She always said that I was her second mom.

I could not speak; I could not think. I was frozen. I touched her. She was cold. I was to agree that she was not alive and could not be saved.

I screamed at my husband.

"Why didn't you save her? Why didn't you want to save her? Why?"

I took my beautiful blue scarf from my dear American mentor and placed it on her cold body. The scarf had been gifted to me with such warmth; it was such a contrast that I was gifting it under such cold conditions.

I couldn't close her open eyes full of suffering and terror. They were expressing her last moments of life. Her life had ended. But why. What for? I couldn't understand and agree with this tragedy. I was frozen on this spring day. I moaned quietly all night long, thinking that she was in a cold place and not with us, with her family.

For sure, my mind shut down. The world was in an enclosed tunnel.

Dear Helen. Dear Helen. My dear Helen.

It was the hardest night of my life.

My stress was too intense. In the morning, I did not recognize anyone except my closest family. I was full of thoughts of my sister only. Either I did not remember them or no one else besides my family was important at that moment.

For ten days afterward, I continued to not recognize faces. People kept visiting us and presenting themselves to me.

"Svetlana, hello, I am your friend. We work together in the same department at university."

It was strange and scary. I was wondering if I was going to be able to improve. I lost memory of all names of authors and books and article titles that I knew so well as a lecturer. I was not sure if I remembered the content of all these sources.

I was supposed to speak at a long-awaited lecture. I arrived at the event and walked to the podium when my name was called. I informed the audience that another lecturer would be stepping into my place, and that I had made the decision to take an indefinite leave of absence. I said goodbye to my department and professional colleagues. There were many people, and I couldn't look into their eyes. I wanted to be strong, but I had no internal power.

I looked down at my text, defeated.

The image of my Helen emerged. She had the strength to fight and stay alive for more than two hours, but she didn't have the help or strength to remain in this world. I realized I must find the strength to live further for her, for my child, for my other sister, for my parents, and for myself.

"I devote this lecture to my beloved sister, Helen, whom I lost recently. This lecture is on my ideal in psychology: Lev Semyonovich Vygotsky."

My memory came to life. I looked over at the head of the Psychology Department and continued to speak. I knew this lecture was my biggest gift and thank-you to Helen. Vygotsky was my idol and favorite for his logic and discoveries, and I was sad that he had died so early in his life.

I received a standing ovation for my lecture and interpretation of Vygotsky's concepts. It was one of the top lectures of my life. I was thankful for my positive perspective, but above all was grateful for Helen's unconditional love for me and for my endless love for her.

Vygotsky saved me, my memory, and shifted my trauma.

Vygotsky was born in Belarus but spent most of his childhood in Gomel. He completed his primary education at home with his mother and a tutor, then graduated from a private Jewish gymnasium. Vygotsky excelled in all academic subjects. His interests as a teenager included arts, literature, history, collecting stamps, playing chess, studying Esperanto, and drafting mostly unfinished theoretical and philosophical manuscripts through the lens of Jewish culture and history. He nearly completed a course of study in law at Moscow University.

Later, Vygotsky presented his investigation comparing different methods in reflexology and psychology at the Psychoneurological Congress in Petrograd. Alexander Romanovich Luria (1902–1977), a research and experimental psychologist, was instantly impressed and invited Vygotsky to collaborate as his junior researcher. This professional relationship established a strong alliance and the formation of what would eventually be known as the Vygotsky-Luria Circle, composed of some of the brightest and leading minds in psychology, education, medicine, physiology, and neuroscience. This network of scholars contributed to the foundation of the integrative science of mind, brain, and behavior.

Vygotsky pioneered the understanding of cognitive and behavioral development, particularly in a social and cultural context.[77]

With Vygotsky at the helm, Vygotsky and Luria connected with Aleksei Nikolaevich Leont'ev (1904–1979), a developmental psychologist with similar aspirations, who sought to define a scientific psychology inclusive of both cognitive and behavioral psychology.[78]

Vygotsky died from tuberculosis on June 11, 1934, at age thirty-seven. Prior to his death, Vygotsky had published more than two hundred original works. A small group of researchers, including Luria and Leont'ev, assembled his works and spearheaded the publication of a six-volume, unabridged collection of Vygotsky's work, *The Collected Works of L. S. Vygotsky.*

As a student of Vygotsky's laboratory, Dr. Masgutova had access to Vygotsky's published and unpublished works.

Shock and denial and the pain and guilt of losing Helen persisted for the next ten or so years.

"She was teaching Vygotsky's zone of proximal development during that time. She showed great promise as a lecturer and researcher. After she died, I was in bad shape. I was trying to work on myself, step by step, to let go," Dr. Masgutova said. "I explored seventeen different belief systems, went to different churches, confessions, synagogues, temples . . . trying to understand why the universe took her soul into the cosmos and why that was her destiny. What was the purpose of losing a beautiful, talented, innocent girl everybody loved? In the midst of this tragedy were wars and catastrophes, and so many more lives were lost. Why all this needless suffering among humanity? I was in conflict with God and the universe. I spent the next ten years looking for the answer. I even went to a psychic from a government agency that is similar to your country's Central Intelligence Agency. I held up a picture of her."

What do you know about this girl?

"They gave some superficial answer, like, that she should live a happy life until she was in her fifties. I stopped trusting them. I even went to the Russian police, several times, and they told me the case was closed.

"The death of this girl broke my heart, and I never got the answers to why she had to die," she said.

Each night, Dr. Masgutova implored Helen to visit her in her dreams.

Helen did not arrive.

Dr. Masgutova began regularly working in the United States on an O-1 visa (an alien of extraordinary ability). Despite the love of her family and colleagues back home, she felt isolated and alone.

Her first fifteen years of marriage to Renat were full of the bliss of young and developing love. Demands made on him were slight. Renat was her first love and the father of their only child. He was the man for whom she cooked and cleaned; she laundered his military uniform, and performed microstretch movements on the sides of his sagittal sutures to release his daily stress as he read the newspaper.

Renat was the man who reset her elbow after she suffered a fall down a railless staircase at the construction site of their new institute in Moscow. During the fall, she consciously leaned toward her left side (to prompt a more automatic bodily response to minimize pain) rather than her right side, which elicited a pain-evoking conscious reaction.

"Renat, I am going to tell you how to help me. The next seven minutes are mine before I'm frozen, in shock, and numb. I do not want to go for surgery. Place your palm over my wrist. Now, pull, twist, and . . ."

For fifteen years, her heart was a full moon, but love, like the phases of the moon, also eclipses, waxes, and wanes. The tides ebbed and flowed, and the gravity of affection felt during travels abroad made her feel like she was lighter, not so weighted down by the angst and suffering from the loss of her sister. The stress took its toll. Meanwhile, Dr. Masgutova's professional career took her in new directions. The couple decided to divorce, yet they continued to live together to bring some level of stability to Denis's life.

Dr. Masgutova had to be true to herself, and to Denis, who also found himself withdrawing from his passion for history, astronomy, and nature.

He became listless and retreated into his room for hours at a time.

"I walked into his room one day, and he was sitting on the bed holding a necklace made of seashells. I did not say anything, and he did not turn around. He knew I was there," Dr. Masgutova said.

"Mama, I do not understand why my Helen would wear this handmade necklace instead of the beautiful gold jewelry she could wear, like her friends do," Denis had said. "She wore this all the time, even to the university. She must have loved me so much. Can you imagine?"

Dr. Masgutova had had a loving childhood, innocent of tragedy and preventable loss when she was his age.

"He had been like a confidant to me during this time, but he had also seemed to become indifferent and disassociated. I knew I had to be there for him," she said.

One night, Helen arrived in Dr. Masgutova's dreams.

"I had not been thinking about her before I went to bed. We hugged for so long in my dream. It was so real," she said.

Helen, I have been waiting so long for this moment. I will move further on with my life, and with Denis. I am letting your soul go. I don't want to hurt your soul any longer. Please, dear Helen, go and be free in the sky, and do your tasks farther on.

"I had always been more like a mother to her. I set the example of how to be serious, disciplined, and responsible," Dr. Masgutova said. "I did not hug her the last time I saw her. After her death, I made the decision—if I want to hug someone, I will hug them. If I want to cry, then I will cry. If I want to pause, stop, laugh, and be free, then I will. That was the day when I accepted that Helen is not with us anymore, and I have a responsibility to continue our good memories. This was the day that I accepted I could help others, including my family and our friends, to live on positively despite such a huge loss.

"I learned to forgive her murderer. His sin was not going to live on inside me. After ten years, I also learned to accept that some questions will always remain unanswered."

Inner peace is not just a feeling. It is a consequence, an outcome, a state of stillness and being. It is action, forward movement, and productivity.

The family continued to live in Russia through the following years, although she and Denis increasingly traveled abroad as the MNRI/Masgutova Method gained ground. They sought to reconcile Helen's loss and debated their own futures. Who would they be? Who could they be? Where should they be?

There were few exceptions for young men in Russia to avoid fulfilling military service. As Denis got older, she increasingly feared that she could lose him as well.

"We could not stay in Russia any longer. I made the decision that the Russian Army will not take my child's life," she said.

Renat's life was taken shortly thereafter when another car smashed into the back end of the car he was driving. He was transported to a hospital in Moscow and died shortly afterward. Dr. Masgutova was notified by the hospital of his admission, and she arrived just in time to say goodbye.

At the turn of the twenty-first century, Dr. Masgutova and Denis packed up their boxes of fairy tales and psychology books, photos, and Nicholas Roerich landscape paintings. They uplifted their roots, hoping to part ways with years of trauma and sad memories. They found comfort in rebuilding their method, furthering the research to justify mainstream acceptance of the Masgutova Method, and mostly, relieving the suffering of others.

IN THEIR WORDS

Scarlett Lewis, Mother and Founder, Jesse Lewis Choose Love Movement
On the morning of December 14, 2012, Jesse Lewis left a note on the family's refrigerator: "Norturting Helinn Love" (Nurturing, Healing Love). He went to school and never came home. He lost his life, along with nineteen of his first-grade classmates and six educators, during the Sandy Hook Elementary School shooting. Law enforcement said that Jesse spent his final moments saving the lives of nine other people.

A lot of people came to Newtown after the tragedy offering trauma relief. My thirteen-year-old son, JT, and I tried working with quite a few of them. We were very open-minded. We wanted to find relief from our trauma. We were exhibiting physical symptoms of sleeplessness and an inability to focus. I hadn't gone back to work. JT hadn't gone back to school full time. We heard about the Masgutova Method/MNRI and decided to try it. Svetlana and her group came to Newtown and were offering free relief programs.

I remember going in for the first time, not really understanding what the program was. The team was incredibly kind and made me feel very welcome.

They explained what trauma does to the body. Everything they said made a lot of sense. It resonated as truth within me. They showed me via reflexes how the trauma was affecting me physically, and then it made even more sense, what they were telling me, how they were retraining my brain, sending messages to my brain that it was safe and how I was operating out of fight or flight.

After that first treatment, I went home and slept that night for the first time. I did feel better. I brought my thirteen-year-old son. No other form of trauma relief was effective for him. The Masgutova Method helped him feel better as well.

I credit Dr. Masgutova and the Masgutova Method with our ability to really get beyond the tragedy, and even turn the tragedy into something that helps make the world a better place.

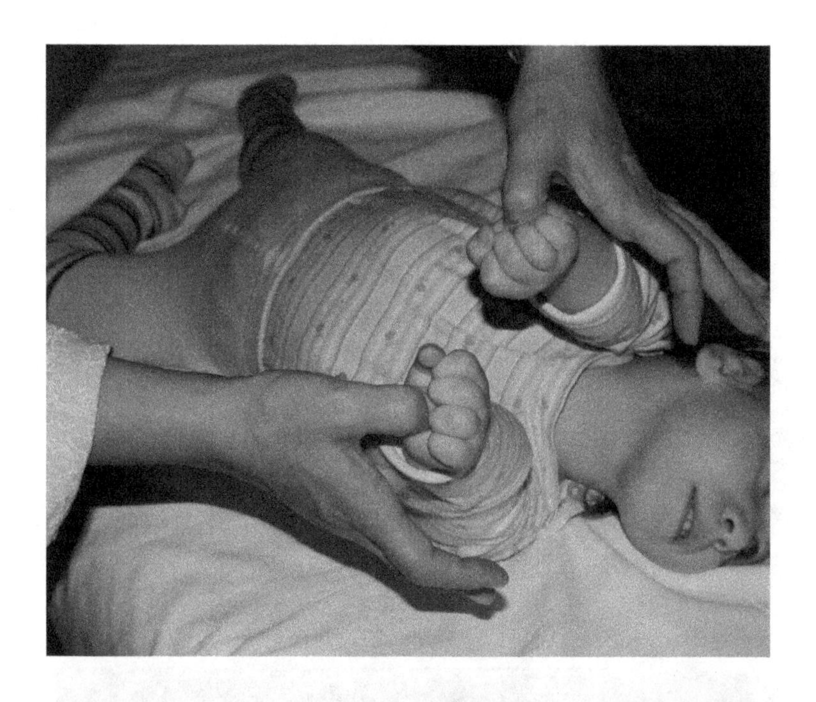

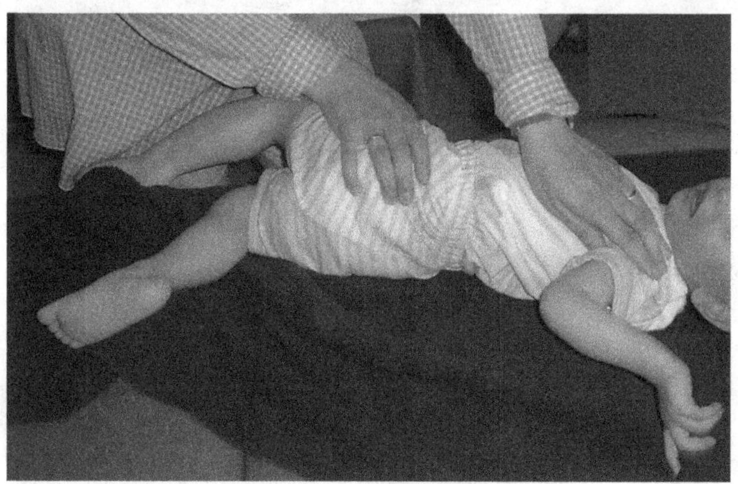

After the Ufa railway disaster, Dr. Masgutova shifted her life's work toward understanding the technical and practical aspects of remodulating reflex patterns, as pictured here and on the following page.

Dr. Masgutova and late her son, Denis, relocated in 1999 from Russia to Poland to build their business.

The effect of Dr. Masgutova's profound trauma recovery work and reflex integration educational programs reverberated beyond Poland. As a result, their organization continued to expand, including to the United States, the Netherlands, Indonesia, Australia, and Singapore, as shown below.

MNRI trauma recovery specialists, including Pamela and Dr. Masgutova, provide MNRI for the survivors of the Sandy Hook Elementary School shooting. The tragic event occurred on December 14, 2012, in Newtown, Connecticut. The team applied MNRI on a voluntary basis with 134 children directly or indirectly affected by the deadliest mass shooting at an elementary school in US history.

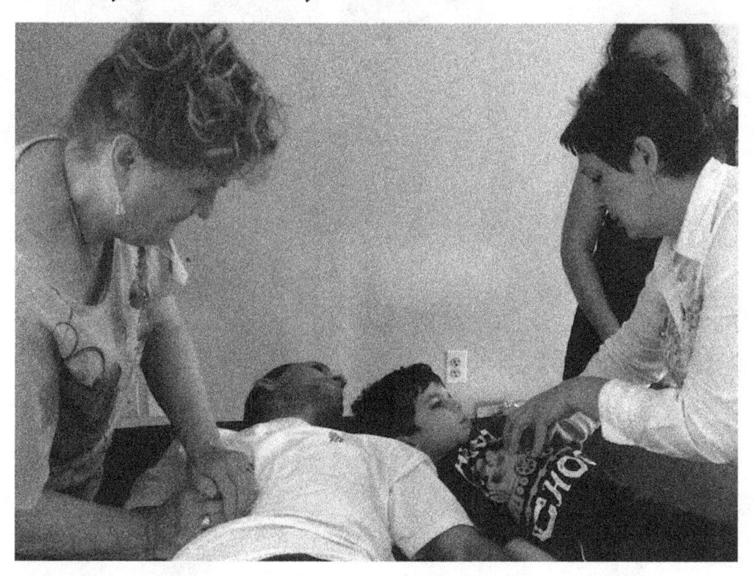

Denis and Ela with their baby, Janek.

A nephew's marriage party is an exciting occasion. From left: Dr. Nelly; her son and the groom, Dr. Eldon; Janek; Dr. Masgutova; and her other nephew, Dr. Elvin.

Denis created about 60 percent of the MNRI program between the ages of about ten and thirty-two.

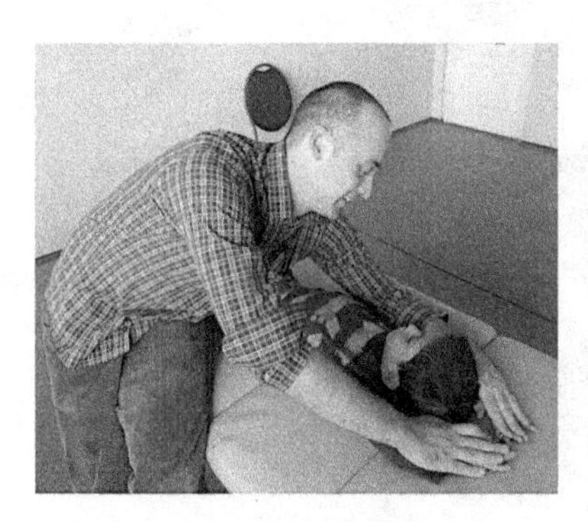

Denis was considered to be extraordinarily gifted. Much like his mom, the more complicated the child's challenges, the more masterful he became.

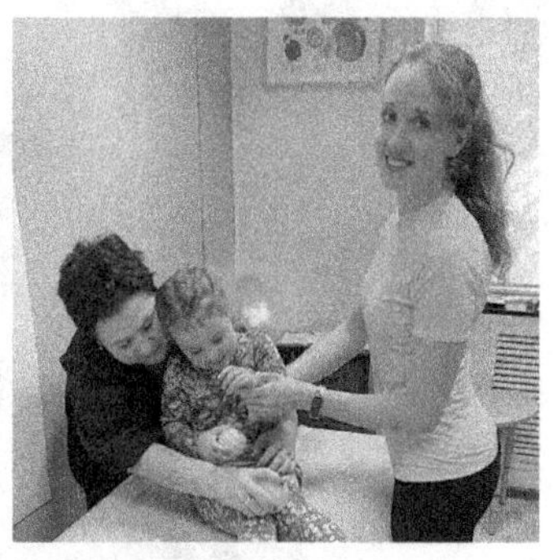

Dr. Masgutova's niece, Dr. Elina, applies MNRI neuromodulation techniques on a child to optimize their neurodevelopment.

Dr. Elvin helps a child improve their head righting and overall strength through MNRI.

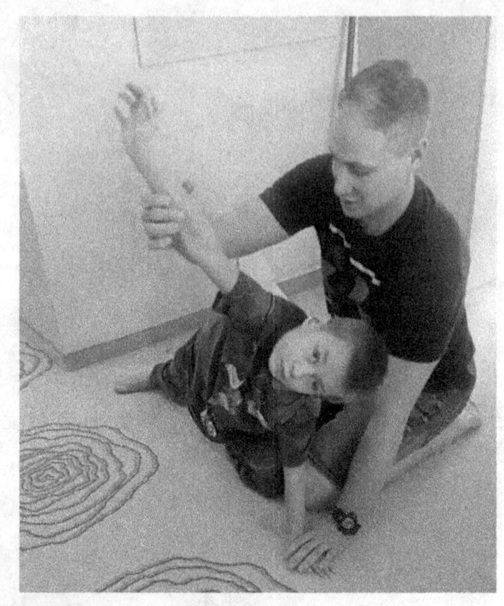

Dr. Masgutova and Isabelle Renard-Fontaine, a pediatric physical therapist and MNRI Instructor and Core Specialist, cradle triplets who just received MNRI.

Dr. Masgutova and Morgan celebrate new growth and success.

Emily has made great progress through MNRI, including initiating eye contact and improving her muscle tone strength. She clearly is happy in the hands of Drs. Nelly and Masgutova.

Above and below: Dr. Masgutova presides over an MNRI hands-on course, MNRI IPET Repatterning and Reflex Integration, at Svetlana Masgutova Educational Institute at the new Lake Nona location in Orlando, Florida. Here, she describes the significance of the discoveries of two 2021 Nobel Prize laureates who have explained how heat, cold, and touch can initiate signals in the nervous system. The MNRI Method is based on facilitating primary reflex integration through specific depths of proprioceptive touch and movement.

Above, left: Dr. Masgutova with SMEI cofounder Pamela Curlee. Above, right: Dr. Patricia Shackleford, dean of the Masgutova Graduate School of NeuroDevelopmental Sciences, with Dr. Masgutova.

Colleagues of the SMEI and Masgutova Graduate School at the Lake Nona Medical Office Building.

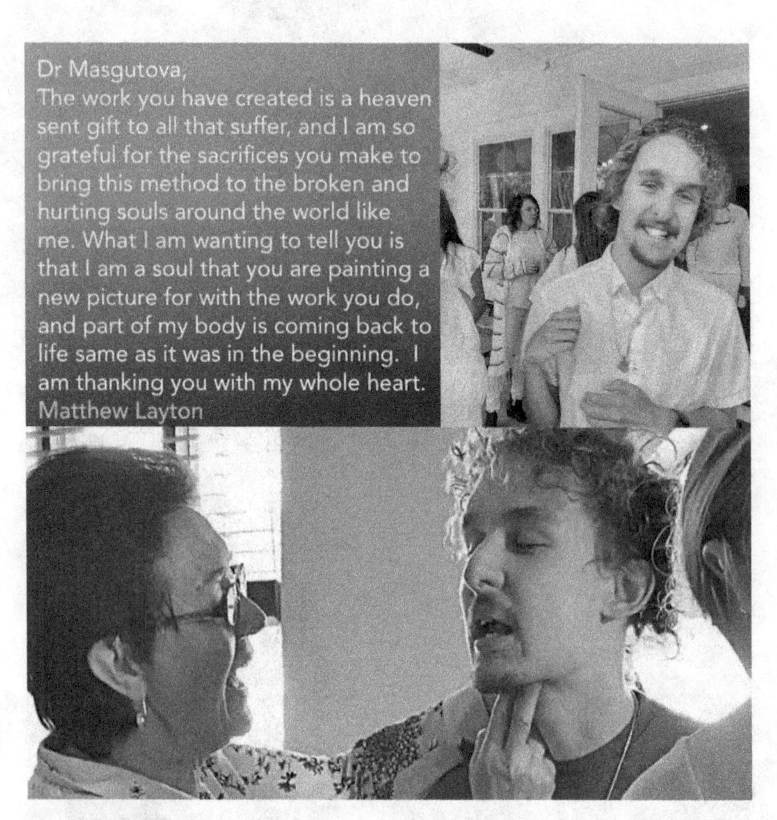

An autistic client typed this message to Dr. Masgutova after an MNRI Family Educational Conference.

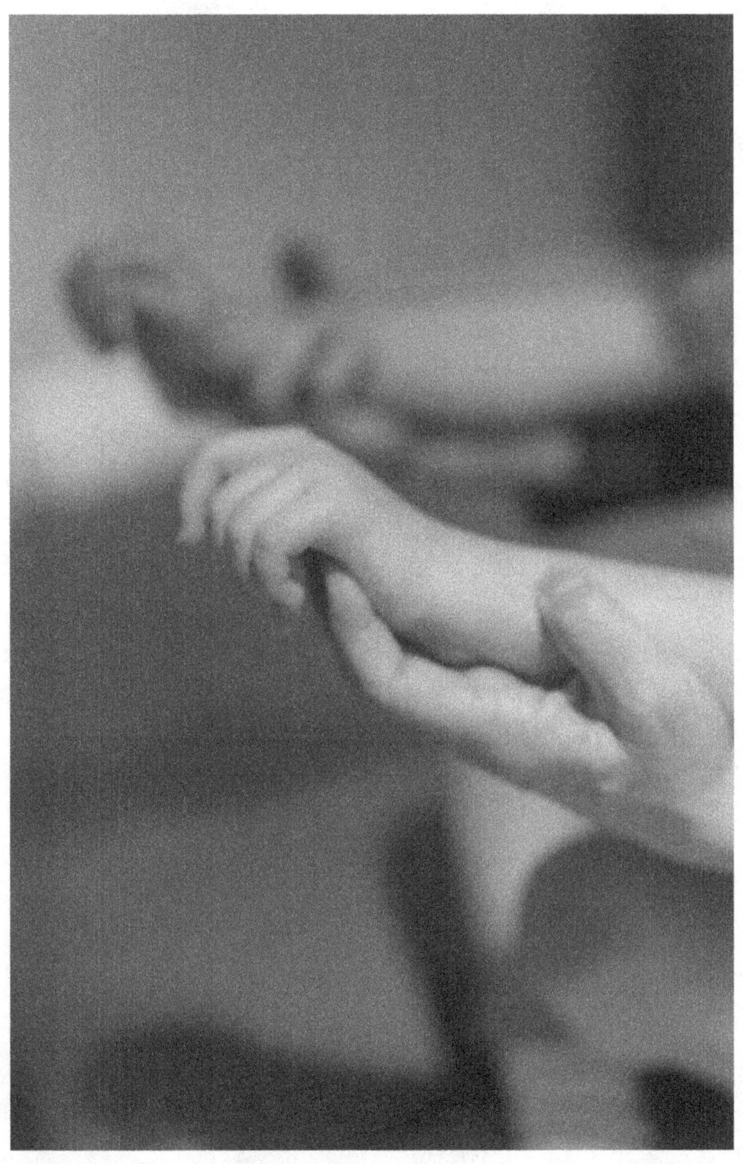

Dr. Masgutova's loving and healing touch has had a profound impact on the lives of thousands of children and adults all over the world, including the writer's son, Daniel.

CHAPTER 9

Going Deeper

The loss of his aunt Helen and then his father affected Denis's academic performance and emotional state.

Like Helen, as a child, Denis had been fun loving, whimsical, and playful. He loved to share and listen to jokes. He was patient and calculated, sculpting entire platoons of tiny Russian soldiers out of clay and demonstrating an early mastery of chess. He was preoccupied with the motion and stillness of nature and the infinite mysteries of the glittering sky of the cosmos. Denis was a thinker and a voracious reader, sponging up the lessons of fairy tales and adult collections of Pushkin and Tolstoy.

For all his accomplishments, he had experienced some learning challenges, particularly with math, physics, and chemistry. He struggled with some of his grades. He had difficulties with writing, so his note-taking speed lagged compared to that of his peers. His lips could not properly differentiate consonants such as "ba" and "pa." While not officially diagnosed, he exhibited the symptoms associated with dyslexia. After the loss of Helen, math and science continued to be a struggle, despite his skill in arts, culture, history, geography, and languages (he eventually spoke five).

His own limitations bridged connections with the populations he served. Denis empathized with those who faced challenges and suffered. He exhibited an aptitude for hands-on work and an insatiable shared curiosity about the questions his mom was seeking to answer.

Eventually, the affable, fun-loving, and charismatic nature of his demeanor returned.

Denis was magnetic and conveyed the characteristics of a well-developed personality: he was humorous and reflective, serious and easygoing, focused and meandering. He was honest, chivalrous, and respectful.

Through the following years, their start-up expanded, providing reflex integration services and education throughout five continents. Denis launched reflex integration rehabilitation therapeutic camps, as his work evolved with challenged clients. He volunteered in Israel to work with soldiers who had PTSD from war. Denis also established free camps to support children from orphanages and victims of physical and criminal abuse in Poland.

Each location's cultural assets were not to be missed. Museums, landmarks, iconic local sites of worship, and national parks were typical places to visit on the itinerary, from the Sequoia National Park in California's Sierra Nevada, to the Nicholas Roerich Museum in New York City, to the tricolored lakes of the volcano Kelimutu in Indonesia.

Nonetheless, they worked long hours, dark to dark, creating multiday conferences that served dozens of children and adults with a spectrum of neurodevelopmental challenges. Each conference day concluded with training sessions for parents, testing specialists-in-training, creating MNRI

Reflex Assessment reports and home programs, conducting hands-on and theoretical research for new program development, and writing manuals for those programs.[79]

Specialists and longtime clients referred to Denis as a "master" and "extraordinarily gifted" in working with children, irrespective of their degree of dysfunction or pathology.

Denis and Dr. Masgutova spent years refining their techniques with programs such as NeuroTactile Integration. They identified torso receptors for activation of breathing and a myriad of visual, auditory, vestibular-proprioceptive, and oral-facial reflex sensory areas. Denis was especially fascinated with the biomechanics of the neck. He developed a complex protocol using submandibular stimulation to activate the coordination of the suck-swallow-breathe process. His techniques demonstrated consequential outcomes in challenged children and adults.

These kinds of dramatic results experienced through their therapy programs continued to shape and refine the MNRI, which expanded from the Poland-based clinic to international educational conferences and post-disaster trauma recovery work. Their post-trauma recovery work became foundational to the MNRI program, opening resources for survival and beyond.

Dr. Masgutova and Denis developed a post-trauma recovery protocol that served those who suffered from conflicts in Israel; survivors of typhoons and earthquakes in the Philippines, earthquakes in Indonesia, and floods in Louisiana; and a community in Newtown, Connecticut, which in 2012 endured what is still the deadliest mass shooting at an elementary school in US history.

POLAND, March 2020—Inside the hall of the International Dr. Svetlana Masgutova Institute in Ursynów, located in the southernmost district of Warsaw, family photos of Dr.

Masgutova, Ela, Denis, and Janek lined the walls. Denis formerly worked here as the cofounder and international director.

Ordinarily, the institute's lobby was full of families entering or leaving the clinic or rehabilitation camp. However, on this particular day, the space was quiet and empty. The Polish government had just notified nonessential businesses that they must close due to the health risks associated with the novel coronavirus.

Dr. Masgutova had a scheduled meeting with a local neurophysiologist. A graduate of the Medical University of Bialystok and founder and clinical coordinator of a neurophysiology center, Dr. Piotr Sobaniec was interested in extending brain-mapping research to children who had specific diagnoses and who were participating in MNRI Family Educational Conferences.

His collaborative work, "Evaluation of the Therapeutic Effect of MNRI Reflex Neuromodulation on Children Diagnosed with Autism Based on Reflex Assessments, QEEG Analysis, and ATEC Questionnaire," was about to be published in the *Journal of Neurology and Neurobiology.*[80]

Thirty children between the ages of six and eleven were evaluated for reflex patterns, brain maps, and social-behavioral-cognitive traits. The MNRI Reflex Assessment, brain wave testing, and Autism Treatment Evaluation Checklist (ATEC) showed substantial positive changes in children with autism spectrum disorder (ASD), including the normalization effect of the MNRI program on the development of reflex patterns and brain wave spectrum (QEEG). These changes indicated improvement in the most challenging developmental areas of life and learning among children with ASD.

This study would be the latest among dozens of published peer-reviewed scientific articles documenting the effect of MNRI, from research involving the changes in brain wave spectrums in children with cerebral palsy to the impact of the modality on neurotransmitter levels associated with inflammatory processes.[81]

Denis pioneered the use of modern technologies and equipment in his research. Electromyography was used to obtain objective data on the muscle responses or electrical activity in response to a nerve's muscle stimulation during reflex integration work. He documented the NeuroStructural program links to milestone changes during a study with more than three hundred children diagnosed with cerebral palsy or ASD. The data informed his further development of new practical techniques in working with sensory and motor deficits, stress, the withdrawal response, and the disruption of breathing reflex patterns.

Mugs of hot tea exhaled steam as they made a soft landing on Dr. Masgutova's conference table. Each accompanying saucer presented a sweet, thin double-layer wafer cookie.

Dr. Masgutova and Dr. Sobaniec faced each other within the frame of the wall-to-wall office window behind them.

He retrieved a glossy-blue folder from the side of his chair and placed it in the center of her conference table.

"We are intrigued by the improvement in neuroplasticity of the brains of the children who participated in neurofeedback research at previous MNRI Family Conferences," he said.

"*Dobrze. Slucham.* Okay. I am listening."

"We are interested in continuing our cooperation. We would like to focus on continuing to use QEEG with children who have the specific diagnosis of autism spectrum disorder and cerebral palsy," Dr. Sobaniec said.

They exchanged pleasantries in English, most likely for my benefit. Talks progressed, and the language shifted into Polish.

Cumulus clouds drifted across the sky. A passing breeze indicated the forthcoming change in air temperature. This persistent breeze rustled the foliage of the evergreen trees that framed the institute. Their branches leaned into the wind. The barren trees bowed beneath the currents. The waltz of nature went on for a while until the wind eased and the tree limbs were still, tranquil, and satisfied with the external conditions.

Indeed, more than thirty-plus years of practical work and research have demonstrated compelling results, and furthering research is a priority of the Masgutova Method. The organization has been focused on developing future research frameworks that will pave the way toward the incorporation of the Masgutova Method within mainstream early intervention and treatment.[82]

IN THEIR WORDS

Teresa Busz, MNRI Instructor, Core Specialist, and International Coordinator and Educational Coordinator at the International Dr. Svetlana Masgutova Institute

I knew her mother's heart was fighting. To comfort her, I wrote,

Denis always had the courage to face the unknown. And he did it differently than we did. We are waiting for you.

His spectacular work, which he performed around the world, has become part of a natural rhythm, facilitating the life and work of many people.

Denis has always taught us that it is worth looking for the best solutions in life and therapy. He was ready for anything to explain, help, name, do, inspire.

He was always ready to give his time.

Denis looked differently at the world, at action, at work, at the sense of success and life.

He always set goals in life and in his daily work. He taught us this boldly and clearly. Set a goal. It is not a simple skill. Nobody taught us this at school. This most important skill is to move forward.

Dr. Svetlana loved Denis unimaginably.

Human life is like a leaf on a tree. They are all born in the spring, beautiful and green. After all, childhood is one of our most beautiful moments in life. Summer shapes the size of the leaf, depending on the location on the branches, the sunshine, and winds of history that do not spare trees or some of the leaves.

Denis did not wait for autumn, a long colorful time when leaves stick to the branches, nor winter, when all the leaves prepare to fall from the tree.

Dr. Svetlana has always said that he gave his family so much joy with his birth.

Denis was an interesting and complicated man.

He always said that we have a 100 percent guarantee for nothing. Certainly, there is no guarantee for life, especially a long life.

The pain the mother experiences, which comes when saying goodbye to her own child, her beloved son, is unimaginable to me.

I looked into Svetlana's eyes and saw this great regret.

Svetlana, you have a beautiful family. I know that with them you will calmly rebuild your strength to find Happy Svetlana. Do it for yourself, for Janek, for others, my heart called. *Your angel will look from heaven and open a wing of hope.*

For every mother who grieves her child, it is a difficult and painful time. Nobody and nothing will compensate her for this separation and loss. And this constant question: Why?

It is a delicate matter, this process of awakening, getting out of the cold. What to do when everything hurts terribly? I know from experience that you can almost always enjoy something if you really desire it. Only, you should desire really hard.

Dr. Svetlana needed us. She needed the touch of her therapy.

To help her, I conducted techniques and exercises from the Stress Hormones and Reflex Integration program.

At first, she wasn't light.

A new period began in her life. Without Denis, but with the responsibilities of his duties and unfinished work. She promised herself that she would try to realize what Denis had started. Day and night, day and night: work. All the time—work, interviews, analysis, preparation, programs, diagnoses, telephone calls, dozens of minor important matters, research, and curriculum development. It is worth working so hard.

We see the great system of the Masgutova Method, seen through Svetlana's and Denis's eyes for a long time.

CHAPTER 10

Time, Space, and Movement

POLAND, March 2020—The Apartament Spalska was located in the Sadyba neighborhood of the Mokotów district in Warsaw. Also known as the "Garden City," for its high number of community and residential gardens, Sadyba was a contrast of modern and historic, parceled into contemporary upper-class housing, new-age retail, and communist-era high-rise apartments. Our planned schedule of in-person interviews concluded in March 2020 in Poland. An impending global pandemic halted the duration of our final overseas destination of Russia. The traffic was sparse due to travel restrictions and business closures that began to occur.

Bundled against the winter's cold, Dr. Masgutova peered up at the five-story apartment building, its neutral exterior distressed with age. Surrounding trees yielded buds with delicate yellow flowers, indicative of a thaw. The Apartament

Spalska, situated within the capillaries of the southern side of Warsaw, was the first apartment in which she and Denis had lived after they left Moscow.

"It was very hard to part ways with our roots, our life, our losses, and to rebuild from zero," Dr. Masgutova said to me as we walked through the residential complex's courtyard.

Dr. Masgutova and Denis had strolled along the sidewalk in front of their apartment to strategize about how to develop and create a logical business growth strategy. Denis desired to pursue higher-education degrees in special education and psychology and to eventually lead the organization. Their vision would enable Dr. Masgutova to focus more on creative pursuits, namely curriculum and method development.

She stopped in front of a tree. The shape of a heart protruded from a section of its chest-level bark.

"We philosophized about business and life, right here," Dr. Masgutova said. "We were mother and son, and professional partners, and we had a symbiotic relationship. We spent long hours talking about life's truths. If he was happy, I was happy. If I was in agony, his soul was in agony. We complemented each other well. We experienced the essence of life when our most challenging cases were presented to us. These were the moments when we paused, stopped, and faced the true value of life in this world," she said.

The previous night, the United States had implemented a thirty-day travel ban to try to slow the spread of the coronavirus. Elsewhere throughout the world, countries were closing their borders. We had been contemplating our options—whether it was safer to stay or leave—but entry and exit strategies imposed different levels of risk and uncertainty. We could have left Poland and traveled to Russia via Belarus, but we were not certain what method of transportation would enable us to get into Russia. Airports were closing. Flights were being cancelled. Additionally, many flight prices were surging in light of the news.

"Can you imagine how life would be different if we had international cooperation?" Dr. Masgutova asked.

I asked her why she thought certain countries appeared to be in a deeper crisis than others, and not just because of the severity of the outbreak. What had prompted different degrees of reaction? What would send the people of one country into a widespread panic, while the citizens of another country took the pandemic in stride?

"Russians are not panicking about the pandemic. We have a history of staying patient and strong when we face a deficit," she said. "In good times, but especially in hard times, we are loyal to each other, and we take care of each other. In our country, it is about the Russian soul."

A voracious, industrious, and innovative worker, Denis loved to integrate with the natural world. He leaped from planes, sailed the seas as a yacht skipper and motorboat helmsman, climbed mountains, traversed the Polish countryside on his motorcycle, and often stood still with nature.

He was fascinated with the concepts of time, space, and movement.

As their method and business matured, Denis focused on enhancing the legacy of his great-great-grandfather's technique by identifying a three-factor activation system that sparks the functional qualities of the body's biomechanical points to improve motor neuron functioning.

He based the development of his technique on three factors: space (place), time (latency), and function (movement), all of which must be in a symbiotic relationship to establish the basis for any development of any process in the world. *Space* signified the precise location of the reflex point. *Time* refers to the specific length of the point's stimulation or zone to affect the timing, speed, and function of a response. The concept of *function* or movement activated the motor/postural aspect of the proprioceptive system of a reflex pattern based on brain processing of the sensory input, and the understanding of what specific motor/gland response must be elicited.

Through his work, Denis found that individuals who suffered were able to retain learned activities, skills, and motor abilities within their bodies for prolonged periods of time.

Activating these points helped correct the dysfunctional or pathological reflexes, so proper development, maturation, and integration of a reflex could occur.

The Kissing Stars points were the hub of transition for motor activity, which triggered the muscular-ligament system to mobilize reflex pattern functioning in different parts of the body.

To know this technique was to be fluent with the inner workings of the body's different systems and how they help facilitate the neurosensorimotor arousal of a reflex pattern. Deep, firm, and flat touch also targeted the proprioceptive system by increasing muscle-tone and tendon regulation. The precision of the action mobilized the Golgi receptors in the intermediate space between muscle fibers and tendons to free the body from its nonproductive state of protection.

Deep touch in the tactile system optimized the body's kinesthetic sensation and awareness and evoked feelings of emotional release and safety.

Certain considerations became more complex as their organization grew. How would they safely and sufficiently scale without sacrificing the quality and integrity of their hands-on method? Which opportunities presented the best outcomes for legitimate advancement, and which opportunities could hinder their goals? What were the risks and benefits associated with larger health-care system mergers, as had been proposed? Despite adversity, they never veered from their vision of ensuring that every child had access to MNRI.

Once, during a ride through the Russian countryside, Denis proposed creating a university that could meet some of their goals. They conceptualized a unique Master of NeuroDevelopmental Sciences degree and doctorate program based on an extensive theory of neuroreflex integration and neurodevelopment.

Just prior to Denis's death, this vision and other plans to further the advancement of the method were in varying stages of development.

By 2016, Denis had earned a post-graduate degree in psychology, but his diploma was withheld because his death occurred two days before the official completion date of study.

On June 7, Denis went to the forest to read, study, and walk. He died shortly after 8:00 p.m. Moscow Standard Time. His official date of passing was listed as June 11, 2016. The circumstances of his death have remained unsolved.

Dr. Masgutova received the call as she was boarding a plane departing from Northern California for Southern California. She dropped the phone and squeezed the knee of her nephew, who was sitting beside her. His kneecap began to bleed. She forbade herself to cry as the plane ascended into the sky, so as not to create in-flight panic. Her flight landed in Southern California, but she didn't leave the airport. She booked the next flight to Moscow. After leaving Moscow, she texted Teresa, on her way to Poland.

> *Dear Teresa, I'm already on a plane with Denis. This is the first time he didn't pay for his ticket on this flight to Warsaw. He has a debt to God. I was allowed to take his urn with me on the plane.*

Teresa responded:

> *Denis always had the courage to face the unknown. And he did it differently than we did. We are waiting for you.*

The borders were closing. Dr. Masgutova and I were running out of time. We attempted to secure plane tickets to Moscow, but our attempts were unsuccessful. The Warsaw Chopin Airport was eerily vacant. Its flight information display system announced nearly all outbound flights were cancelled.

Her daughter-in-law, Ela, secured a shuttle that transported Dr. Masgutova and me through the Polish and German countryside and eventually toward the Frankfurt Airport, where we secured passage on one of the last airplanes departing for the United States.

The day before we left Poland, we paid our respects to Denis.

"I did not tell anyone about Denis—only our closest friends and family members knew," Dr. Masgutova said. "Ela, Janek, and I arrived from the car, holding Denis, and holding our heads up high. We saw over a hundred individuals from our MNRI family, gathering to support us. Can you imagine? I was carrying the ashes of my son."

She spent time with him, and I gave her space.

After his death, she barely paused in her work; although, surrendering to the greatest loss of her life certainly would have been justified.

She credited Denis with contributing about 60 percent of the content of the MNRI program, but together, they still had many unfinished plans and big goals.

Denis had ambitious visions—the development of more advanced-level courses and building specialized equipment and toys for challenged children that would promote reflex integration. He had begun developing theories of how reflex patterns could support the executive functions of the cortex based on Luria's concepts of encoded brain integrity. Denis had sketched the curriculum for a university that would feature both a master's level and a doctorate program in reflex integration and neurodevelopment, with the goal of furthering the method's inroads into an interdisciplinary system of whole-person care that would be supported with the latest knowledge and research in reflex integration and neurodevelopment.

Denis was also in the process of developing computer-assisted robotics technologies that would help him more deeply understand the biomechanics of the body. This incredible work, stored in two computers, would never be recovered.

How many more lives would they have changed together? What would they have continued to build, and what could it have become?

The same month Denis died, in June 2016, Dr. Masgutova worked an eight-day MNRI Family Conference in Minnesota. She did not pause throughout her full schedule of global conferences and clinics. The volume of reflex assessment work provided her solace as she attempted to move forward.

She published a journal article on the effects of the MNRI post-trauma recovery for the child victims of the mass shooting in Newtown and finalized a book, *Post-Trauma Recovery: Gentle, Rapid, and Effective Treatment with Reflex Integration*, which was published in 2018 under the co-authorship of Denis.

About a year after his death, Dr. Masgutova and her leadership team forged ahead with their plans to launch a US-based university.

A global pandemic would present a new obstacle in her efforts to carry out their unfinished work. This period would have been a time for pause and rest, a sensible proposition for an organization whose work is dependent on touch.

"We are compressed by time," Dr. Masgutova often has said.

I recalled the words of Father Jaroslaw Szymczak, chairman of the global organization Family Support Foundation. He is one of Dr. Masgutova's closest friends and confidants, a priest from Poland, who carried Denis's ashes to their final resting place.

"Why can't God give her forty-eight hours in one day?"

I was about to see the cost. The forthcoming weeks and months would not be easy. She would work dark to dark through a disruptive global pandemic to serve challenged children and adults, who badly needed touch, through videoconferencing applications and smaller-sized, CDC-guided in-person events.

Within a few months of the forthcoming global lockdown, Dr. Masgutova will have conducted and/or spearheaded the development of a suite of new programs, including manuals and videos with exercises to support stress resilience, immunity, and well-being for people; the launch of an online lecture series to promote interdisciplinary scientific research, which would reach parents and professionals in forty countries; online MNRI consultations; and an expansion of online courses. After years of planning and development, Dr. Masgutova and a nonprofit board of directors would fulfill a longtime dream of opening a university-level program, with the unveiling of the nonprofit Masgutova Graduate School of NeuroDevelopmental Sciences within the nonprofit Masgutova Foundation 501(c)(3) registered public charity.

I would be with her in her kitchen during a two-week quarantine, cradling a mug of tea well into the night.

Among a juggle of many priorities, the tension of the external circumstances would recall the broader perspective. I would detect an air of impatience as I was guiding the questioning oriented at her. She would redirect some biographical questions to the tasks at hand.

"I want this book to focus on outreach," she would say.

"This is about sharing the knowledge and helping as many people suffering as possible."

A visit to Denis preceded this transformative moment in time.

On a crisp winter day, March 16, 2020, in Poland, I raised my chin to the blue sky and warmth of the sunshine.

I closed my eyes and thought of the other families I interviewed at different MNRI Family Educational Conferences who realized hope and life's potential through the Masgutova Method.

IN THEIR WORDS

Renee Stoklosa

In early 2016, we met the love of our life when our daughter, Emily, was born. I was induced at my forty-week appointment, and she was born at forty weeks and one day. I had a smooth pregnancy but a long labor with vacuum-assisted delivery. I did not meet her initially because she did not cry. But after several minutes with the doctors, she did. They laid Emily on my chest, and I fell in love so hard. We were told she looked healthy and had an Apgar score of nine. I had anticipated exclusively breastfeeding her, but she demonstrated dehydration, so the nurses took her to be bottle-fed.

She had high bilirubin levels (jaundice), but they were within reason, and we were discharged. The next few days were filled with adventures, the kind I thought most new parents experienced. We had been readmitted for a few days for her bilirubin and subsequent dehydration. It was recommended we see an orthopedist for a hip click. The issues were resolved, and we went home to enjoy our little bundle of joy all to ourselves.

At two months, we noticed Emily's head constantly turned to the right. She had mild torticollis. At three months, she still had trouble with head control, but she did have a large head in proportion to the rest of her body. She felt very soft, like she sunk when I picked her up. Her doctor wasn't concerned, though, saying she should grow into her head size and get stronger. We were happy to believe that. She was, after all, happy, social, and curious.

At seven months old, Emily still had poor head control, could only roll from tummy to back, and had much difficulty grasping objects. She babbled and blew raspberries, but her voice was very soft. We saw a neurologist, who ordered every test possible, including an EEG, MRI, and nutritional, genetic, eye, and ear tests. The MRI gave us some information, but ultimately the results were inconclusive. The genetic tests indicated two mutations: one inherited from Daddy, and the other was de novo. Neither was used to explain her vast motoric delays.

Ultimately, she was diagnosed with hypotonia and nothing more.

At nine months, she began PT, OT, and ST (speech-language therapy) for sixty minutes each per week. We took her to see pediatricians, a top geneticist, two neurologists, and an ophthalmologist at a world-renowned health-care facility. We asked what else we could do to help her. We were met with the usual responses: "She is progressing, so that is good. Continue her therapies." When we asked if there was anything nutritionally that we could do, we were told, "No supplementation or medicine would help because her growth is normal, and she's tested negative for mitochondrial disease."

And they would all say, "Just keep doing what you're doing."

That last statement really bothered us.

Emily was nine months old but very behind. She had some head control but tired quickly. She could not pull-to-sit or sit independently. Her highest-level motor skill was a labored roll.

She was fed with purées, and many times would gag or vomit. There was a long lag in her motor planning. She was interested in others and social, but passive because she couldn't do anything motorically. Her therapies were centered around using a mobile stander, AFOs (ankle-foot orthoses), and a SPIO (Stabilizing Pressure Input Orthosis) vest, and she was not making gains.

Her eyes were bright and curious. She was always engaged. But her world was limited by her body.

We could not keep doing what we were doing.

Time went on, and we continued early intervention but always sought other treatments. We tried different therapies beyond the traditional route. We even traveled to Europe for nearly six months to try a therapy not done in the US, with little success. And then, we found MNRI when she was two and half years old. Her motor skills were the same at that time, but just a little stronger.

After a session with a local MNRI Core Specialist, Emily was visibly changed. She had a vitality we had never seen before. She held her head strongly for the entire car ride home. She had the energy to play for hours afterward when she normally would have needed to nap. We went for a second session and had the same experience. The next day, we booked airline tickets to have her assessed by Dr. Svetlana Masgutova.

Emily is now four, and it has been one and a half years since our first family conference. I now understand her reflexes were asleep, but her nervous system is healthy.

MNRI has awakened her reflexes.

Emily's motor skills have changed dramatically. Her visual auditory processing, speech, receptive language, social skills, and cognition have greatly improved. She no longer is a prisoner of her body. She reaches milestones and is proud of herself. She understands words and emotions and tries to communicate. She is smart enough to be mysterious and funny. Her muscle tone has increased. Emily is rolling according to the proper pattern. She pulls to sit, and army crawls a little. She understands anything she has learned and is trying to say a few words. She eats thick purées and does not gag or vomit. Other children are interested in her, and she actively plays with them.

We are so proud of her and excited for the future. Yes, she is on her own timeline, but she has no ceiling that we can see. There was a time when I could not conceive how it would be possible for her to get off the floor, let alone have a chance at an independent life. But now she does.

Because of Dr. Masgutova's work, we will proudly and gratefully keep doing what we are doing. And we can't wait to see what comes next for our Emily.

▲

Diane Colonnese

Svetlana has saved Lily Grace from many surgeries and has changed the course of her life. My husband and I are eternally grateful for her. We don't know where we would be without her.

Lily was born prematurely at twenty-seven weeks. She was immediately admitted to the NICU for respiratory distress and sepsis. She received numerous diagnoses, including stridor, chronic lung disease, patent ductus arteriosus, pneumonia, anemia of prematurity, IVH grade 1, apnea, gastroesophageal reflux, inguinal hernia, hyperbilirubinemia, retinopathy of prematurity, and vocal cord paralysis. She also had severe sensory processing disorder due to being in the NICU for over four months. Tactile, sensory, or auditory stimuli were very painful for her. Lily startled and cried all the time, but she had no voice. Her mouth contorted into a silent cry, and I would cry right with her.

The doctors prepared us for the worst: that she would not walk, talk, or eat, and likely would be institutionalized.

She was intubated multiple times and had a hernia surgery, a Nissen fundoplication to help stop the reflux, and the placement of a feeding tube. She also had hereditary multiple exostosis, also known as bumpy bone disease. Her cartilage was white when she had her first X-rays. My husband, Gary, has the same disease, and he's had over twenty surgeries throughout his life.

Lily received multiple therapies and early intervention once she was home from the hospital. She had a compromised immune system and was sick often, so progress was minimal. We did not know what else to do.

We heard about Dr. Svetlana Masgutova through a mutual friend who knew SMEI cofounder Pamela Curlee. Lily was eighteen months old by this time, and she could not sit, crawl, walk, talk, eat, or leave the house. We invited Svetlana and Pamela to stay with us, en route to a conference in California.

They arrived at midnight, when Lily was sleeping, and they immediately began to work on her on breathing reflex repatterning and stress hormones release. We were a little uneasy having strangers in the house, but her body instantaneously was at peace when they began to quietly work with her.

The following day, Lily was joyful as they worked with reflexes such as Babinski, Foot Tendon Guard,* Spinal Perez, and Trunk Extension. Her body responded beautifully. Lily was able to bear weight and learned how to properly cross crawl. Within days, Lily began walking, and three months after Svetlana's visit, she had mastered a five-hundred-word vocabulary.

We apply the MNRI Home Program exercise techniques and attend MNRI clinics or conferences twice a year. Now, Lily is incredibly smart with an expansive vocabulary. She dances, plays piano, and has played starring roles in school theater. We continue to see Svetlana through educational clinics a couple times per year.

Lily has only had one surgery in her entire life. She has

some of the best orthopedic doctors in the world, and they are incredulous.

▲

Marissa Vaccaro

Our MNRI journey began after I saw some information online about reflex integration.

Emma had an exaggerated startle reflex and a very sensitive sensory system. We were looking for a method to address these issues. We signed up for an MNRI Family Educational Conference and were hooked after day one. The input that MNRI provided Emma's body was exactly what she had been craving.

Her body became relaxed, and most importantly, she enjoyed getting on the table to have her sessions. To our surprise, the changes we have seen in Emma far exceeded our expectations of helping her Fear Paralysis Reflex. Emma has made many improvements in her development, including eating by mouth, living with a calm body, reduced Fear Paralysis Reflex, using her hands more functionally, making more vocalizations, reducing her arching, and experiencing overall comfort in her own body and skin.

From the beginning, Dr. Masgutova has been so kind, caring, and comforting, all while really letting us know what we needed to do to help Emma. She has played a key part in Emma's journey in life.

I hope that all children who need this input can experience the joy that MNRI has brought to Emma and our entire family.

▲

Erin Manahan

My daughter, Nora, was born with a malformed right hemisphere of her brain. She had a complete right anatomic hemispherectomy, which involves the removal of the frontal, parietal, temporal, and occipital lobes. The deeper structures, such as the basal ganglia, thalamus, and brain stem, are left in place. She wasn't using language functionally, and I felt like we were running out of time. She was not making developmental progress during her first year of life. She had seizures in utero, which continued until the age of three.

My daughter skipped developmental phases because of her seizures and her medication-induced fog. She then had her second brain surgery at age three and a half to stop the seizures. We began seeing a speech and language therapist, and she introduced us to MNRI. It was a long drive to her office. We were wondering if this was a good use of our time. Was this the right therapy?

We attended our first MNRI Family Educational Conference with Dr. Masgutova.

MNRI rewrote milestones we were informed would never happen—that she would ever crawl, talk, or open her hands.

Nora is now five, and she is not the same child she was even six months ago. She is finishing sentences now and making word approximations. She is using language in a meaningful way, demonstrating problem-solving skills, and fully accepting of our touch.

▲

Jade Kim

We adopted our child, Leon, when he was eleven months old from an orphanage. His mother had the baby and left the hospital the next day. He spent two weeks in the hospital alone, which was very traumatic for him. We do not think he was hugged or touched in a loving way. He achieved his milestones, though they always were late. He was diagnosed with sensorimotor integration issues and dyspraxia. He also has ADHD and social (pragmatic) communication disorder.

Leon was very attached to us, but he also had a fear that something would happen to his father or me. His fears and challenges affected his studies at school. He could read a book and recite the details, and his spelling was excellent, but if he tried to summarize what he had just read, he struggled to form a proficient and coherent summary. We tried neurofeedback, neuropsychologists, you name it.

We attended our first MNRI conference, and it wasn't easy in the beginning. Our son was very hyperactive. After the conference, Leon was a different child. He was no longer struggling to complete his sentences. There was more logic to his thought process. His teacher said he's been asking a lot of questions and is very curious. We want him to be proud of himself and his heritage and rise above life's challenges. This method helped us achieve those goals.

There were many such heartfelt testimonials, expressing gratitude for developmental outcomes realized through the Masgutova Method. I thought of my own child's experience.

Daniel has continued to blossom and defy the limited developmental roadmap that we were told to expect during his childhood. He can now sit independently, with minimal support. My husband and I have discussed the possibility that we may not need a wheelchair-accessible vehicle. We no longer use a blender for pureeing food, nor thickening agents for liquids. He transitioned to water and has enjoyed different textured foods. The improvements in his posture and stability have afforded him the chance to begin walking with assistance. He has become curious, contemplative, and happy. He has initiated speech and has continued to bring us joy with new developmental and milestone gains, milestones that we were told we could not imagine as likely during his childhood.

The gait trainer has been in the garage. The blender has

collected dust under our cabinet. We cancelled the monthly order of xanthan gum thickener, as Daniel has been able to drink water with no complications.

There is no ceiling in the development of a human, just a beautiful, endless blue sky open with possibilities.

The light of her only son has lived on through Dr. Masgutova, and her light through him and their family, and children and adults all over the world who have been touched by the life-giving method of MNRI. To experience the essence of MNRI is to be changed with the full perspective of the journey to the results.

I walked toward her, as she cradled a lit candle in front of Denis's memorial. Her face was moist with tears, but she had a peaceful smile.

"I work for Denis's soul, to see that his work continues. In the days before his death, he developed a new program for parents, on biomechanics, shock absorption, and reflex patterns, to help improve the life quality of their children. I could not pause and so continued to teach this program in the days after his death. He cared so much for the people who suffered.

"I made the decision to work for two people. I hope I am coming closer to realizing the completion of some of those plans. I want him to be proud of me. He used to give me long hugs, so full of presence, and very unique. He said to me, 'Mama, feel this momentum.'"

I opened my arms to hug her. My left arm gently drew her back closer to me, while my right hand reflexively cradled the nape of her neck into my shoulder. We were still, in this position, for some time.

We extracted ourselves from our embrace. Our outstretched hands remained linked.

There were still words to say. They were the words that, at this moment, have never felt more real, reaching from my mother's heart into her mother's heart. These words embodied the gratitude of many individuals whose lives she has touched.

"I love you," I said.

We began to move forward. Our left hands folded into one another. Our right hands reached to meet each other to close the infinity loop. I intended to place my right hand above hers, in a reflexive intent to protect her. Instead, her right hand found its proper place, at the top.

EPILOGUE

The Gift of Her Touch

She is a psychologist, a scientist, a creator, an entrepreneur, and an international humanitarian. She is a daughter, a sister, an aunt, a grandmother, and a godmother to even nonfamily members. A dear friend to hundreds, maybe even thousands of people. A citizen of Russia and of the United States, and also a citizen of the world.

She is a mother. She is a survivor.

Recovery will follow through our work. I felt this and learned how to thrive and go further on with development despite the trauma of losing my sister and my one and only child. Inspired by the principles of Vygotsky, activating the regulation of our brain-body system will help us shift through true life experience and move from reaction to action. After survival, there is space for development and joy. My goal is to build happiness.

People say they love her humanity. People say they value that she can feel their pain and that she can transform that pain into significant life changes.

If we want to realize change, we need to reach into our inner developmental potential. This is the source of our strength.

They say she is a healer, like her great-grandfather. That everyone in her family has the Gift, in different ways, but that her touch is unique. How could it not be, for all the pain and suffering she has taken in, and all the healing and results she has given back?

We want to touch the strength of the person, to reach their power from within. Each person is a creator. Our children and the people around us are our biggest life teachers. We want to apply techniques that support the positive developmental mechanisms that are the source of their power to create change. We want to alleviate suffering.

I was invited for a trauma recovery session about five months after our initial interview for this book. The light streamed in through the window.

"Are you ready?" she asked.

"Yes," I whispered.

I looked into her eyes as she placed her hands above my shoulders. Her palms lowered into the pectoralis major clavicular on my chest. I felt her touch deeply. Her hands remained there for several seconds. Her hands glided down to my wrists, where they paused for a brief proprioceptive stretch. I felt my body lean down and in toward her.

"What is your name?" she asked.

"Kathy," I whispered.

"What is your name?"

Stronger.

"Kathy," I stated, louder.

"What are your goals?"

"My goal is to be the strongest mother I can be," I said. "I don't want my child to be in pain. I want him to be happy."

My chest began to heave, and I could not control my tears.

She commanded the space around the table, moving from

one side to the other, as she applied several MNRI Reflex Assessment techniques on my feet, arms, and body core.

"Asymmetry," she said. "Your body is in protection. We have a lot of work to do. We are going to facilitate the goal-setting for psychosomatics. Are you open to bringing positive change? Are you open to transition? Do you invite more light and strength into your life?"

"Yes," I said between the shallow rhythm of my inhale and exhale. "I am open to positive change and transition. I invite more light into my life."

I felt her fingers descend deep into a point on my abdomen, which she described as the upper-left rectus abdominis.

"Then let's be open to courage. We will have several goals: I am open to contentment and joy in my life. I am open to the small and big gifts of the world . . ."

She placed her hands on my sternum, near my heart, and issued five slow and deep taps. *Cha-cha, cha-cha-cha.* She repeated the exercise on the ends of my deltoid muscles and hips. I recognized the Fear Paralysis exercise as one that I work on with my own son, twice per week.

I closed my eyes and saw a younger version of myself. She was seated in a wheelchair, wearing a blue hospital gown and trying to reach into an Isolette, where her newborn baby lay tethered with many cords around his heart, head, and nose. Baby boy Daniel was wrapped in a blue swaddle that had a sticker on it: *Property of the hospital.* The girl was crying. I could see the neonatologist, who asked her if she had been taking drugs or drinking during her pregnancy before he delivered the news to her that her newborn son had a genetic condition.

I could not breathe. I opened my eyes, looked down, and saw my lifted rib cage.

I felt her fingers press into the sides of my body, and they moved in a circular motion, down and away from my spine.

She tapped while I inhaled and exhaled. Using a flat, deep pressure, she stretched in the direction of the growth of the muscle fibers, anteriorly, inferiorly, and laterally.

I wanted to tell the girl that she was strong and that she was chosen for this life path for a much deeper reason.

Her fingers paused and pressed into different sections of my back to strengthen my spine.

The brave boy in the Isolette will show her what it means to transition from a diagnosis of failure to thrive, to thriving. He will show her what the meaning of life feels like. She will feel it through the pain but also through each heartfelt moment of joy when they realize milestones little and big through a method of neurodevelopment created by a woman who will forever change their lives.

I felt her cupped hands embrace each segment of my arms and the lower parts of my legs.

"Tell her you want to give her a choice," Dr. Masgutova softly said.

Her fingers bowed and clicked, fluttering over my knee joints, upper legs, and quadriceps. She delivered the quick-release techniques at precise reflex trigger points to evoke the reintegration of reflexes that would support the release of stress hormones and trauma.

I approached the wheelchair, and invited my younger self, holding her baby, into my arms.

"Our goal is to build happiness. Our goal is to become stronger and grow and develop further on. Our goal is to do and be our best with the gifts we have been given."

Her work continued.

I could hear Dr. Masgutova's family members in the other room. They were preparing food and hot tea for a woman they barely knew. First, I was to rest before I joined them. Meanwhile, other family members were inbound; their plane was about to land.

There were a lot of people waiting for her, wanting to receive the gift of her touch, the gift of her.

She raised my arms up and then appraised my legs with the same intention. Symmetry. My breathing was even and deep. She wiped the remaining teardrops from my face. I felt full of light.

Dr. Masgutova nodded in approval and softly said, "For now, we are done."

From hip to foot, she swept her hand down each leg with a flourish, the signature stroke of her genius, signing off on another masterpiece.

At the time of this book's publishing, the Svetlana Masgutova Educational Institute relocated to the Lake Nona Medical Office Building in Orlando, Florida, where globally recognized medical and educational institutions, vibrant culture, innovation, and holistic well-being intersect. The not-for-profit Masgutova Graduate School of NeuroDevelopmental Sciences' Master of Science degree program was well under development, with its inaugural students targeting graduation, and paving a pathway toward the school's accreditation.

IN THEIR WORDS

Quotes from selected former and current research and education collaborators who also aspire to increase the visibility and awareness of the MNRI/Masgutova Method

Jay R. Lucker, EdD, CCC-A/SLP, FAAA, Certified and Licensed Audiologist and Speech-Language Pathologist Specializing in Auditory-Processing and Language-Processing Disorders
As a certified and licensed audiologist and speech-language pathologist, I find great interest in Dr. Masgutova and the Masgutova Method. This led me to complete a research study on the correlation between children's delays in developing primary reflexes and auditory-processing skills (their abilities to take in and make sense of what they hear). We found significant correlations between areas of auditory-processing disorders and primary reflex problems, indicating that improving the children's primary reflexes would likely contribute to improvements in their auditory-processing abilities.

▲

Henry Kaiser, PsyD, MBA, Former Trustee of the Kaiser Family Foundation and a Director of Kaiser Foundation Health Plans
The profession of neurosensorimotor reflex integration (MNRI) has the paradoxical status of an extensive history of development, vigorous physical and online training, academic research facilities, and a growing cadre of providers throughout Europe, North and South America, and Asia, and yet at the same time being relatively unknown and poorly understood by the mainstream medical community. Its development has been the result of a dedicated leader who began her work in

Russia, building on scholarly work and publications not well known in the West.

The not-for-profit Masgutova Foundation and the not-for-profit Masgutova Graduate School of NeuroDevelopmental Sciences augment the work of the Svetlana Masgutova Educational Institute in reaching both families and developmental professionals who service these families to bring to the global health-care system a recognition of the efficacy and importance of optimum neurosensory reflex integration based on the natural innate functions of the body.

The Svetlana Masgutova Educational Institute and the Masgutova Foundation are material pillars for a conceptual structure being implemented to reach families and the many different professions who service these individuals through stress and trauma reduction to enhance their lives. They offer well-designed programs and activities. In addition, they aspire to bring to global health care and well-being a deserved recognition of the importance and efficacy of optimal reflex integration for post-trauma recovery and the development of a resilient central nervous system to effectively resolve the consequences of dysfunction stemming from stressful events.

▲

Jaroslaw Lucas Koberda, Neurologist

I was invited by Svetlana to do research with MNRI, and our involvement lasted approximately one year. We collected the brain waves from clients with different neurological, psychiatric, and neurodevelopmental disorders and created brain maps. We collected the brain waves before and after MNRI therapy and investigated the response to this therapy. Our findings concluded the very positive effects of MNRI therapy on the functional performance of the brains of affected individuals.

We noticed marked improvements in previously dysregulated brain wave patterns after application of this therapy. We also were told by patients or their parents that MNRI therapy resulted in both subjective and objective improvement in the clinical performance of their loved ones. It is my impression that manual therapy delivered by MNRI practitioners has very positive neuromodulatory properties.

Therefore, by completion of the treatment, clients may benefit from its neuroplastic effects, resulting in better brain connectivity and function. This frequently manifests as a reduction of cognitive dysfunction, neurological impairment, or symptoms related to traumatic brain injury, PTSD, and anxiety.

Based on my observations, we may conclude that MNRI therapy is considered to be a new form of neuromodulation technique similar in effectiveness to neurofeedback and transcranial magnetic stimulation.

Svetlana and her international MNRI team have impressed me with their dedication and passion toward the well-being of their patients in achieving great outcomes. In addition, I believe more neurologists and other clinicians should consider utilizing MNRI services for the benefit of their patients.

▲

Gretchen L. Stewart, PhD, MNRI Parent
and Founder and Director of Smart Moves Academy

My son was diagnosed with autism spectrum disorder at age three. The changes are visible in my son after attending an MNRI conference. I always take before and after pictures, and everyone is amazed at the physical changes they see. With the intensive, deep reflex work he needs, MNRI is the only method we have found that gets his reflexes working as nature intended. The cognitive changes are what excite me the most. He is more present and attentive, and his reaction and processing times are much faster after MNRI. I believe MNRI is one of the primary keys to an independent future for him.

As founder and director of Smart Moves Academy, the first US nonprofit private school to optimize learning through movement, I am passionate about bringing this method to more children. Smart Moves Academy recognizes the triune nature of development in childhood as brain, body, and environment. MNRI as a curriculum for both brain and body could not be a more natural and effective partner in helping us deliver on our promise to parents and children of an education that optimizes brain performance through physical activity for lifelong learning, health, fitness, and emotional well-being.

▲

Heather Tallman Ruhm, MD, Medical Director at Documenting Hope, a Cornerstone Research Program of Epidemic Answers, a 501(c)(3) Nonprofit Organization Dedicated to the Prevention and Reversal of Chronic Health and Developmental Conditions in Children

The complexity of modern illnesses demands a multitargeted systems approach, both for analysis and intervention. Chronic illness is a total-load issue, with imbalances due to deficiencies and excesses, including a variety of toxins and traumas. As researchers from the Documenting Hope Project—which encompasses two IRB-approved studies: CHIRP, a comprehensive health and exposure survey, and FLIGHT, the prospective study of a collaborative community-based model of bio-individualized medicine—we were drawn to the impressive work of Dr. Svetlana Masgutova and her trained practitioners.

Dr. Masgutova has a remarkable understanding of the diverse roles and functions of neurosensorimotor reflexes and what their status teaches us about balances or imbalances in the human body. Her work has given us another validated tool to assess, measure, and support a bio-individualized and carefully sequenced intervention plan for children with modern chronic illnesses. We appreciate all the years of dedication and ongoing research to bring us this valuable tool called MNRI, which is helping us document hope for children in need of genuine health transformation.

We know that many generations will benefit from this work.

ACKNOWLEDGMENTS

I saw the invitation to donate in Denis Masgutov's name on the Masgutova Method website shortly before attending our first MNRI Family Educational Conference in 2018. Like the plaque on the wall of the former SMEI Center, the post indicated Denis had died two years earlier. The donations aimed to further the cause of growing and expanding the Masgutova Method as a tribute to Denis's life. As a mother, my heart ached. How could one mother who unexpectedly lost her son continue to persevere through such agony? A genius whose work self-heals through healing others who suffer. The more complicated the child, the more masterful she becomes. A mother's uncompromising commitment to further the unfinished work of her son, whose own aptitude revealed its highest expression through the most challenging of cases. I knew at that moment that I wanted to tell her story and give back all book sale proceeds to continue to benefit the work of the Svetlana Masgutova Educational Institute and Masgutova Foundation.

A lot of love went into writing this book.

A special thanks to Tricia Borsch for sharing her personal story and encouraging us to register for our first MNRI Family Educational Conference. Deep thanks to Pamela Curlee for taking my hand and forwarding the email. Thank you to Isabelle Renard-Fontaine for inspiring our journey during our first MNRI conference session and for saying yes to this book idea. I spoke with dozens of MNRI families and professionals for this project. I am incredibly grateful to each of you for sharing your story.

Special thanks to the Svetlana Masgutova Educational Institute administration staff, including but certainly not limited to Sally Averkamp, Tricia, Geri Brady, Nora Keller, Rebekah LaVone, Tina Marks, Jessica Rife, and Candice Wade, for all the work you do to support families and professionals. This sentiment of gratitude extends to MNRI instructors, specialists, event organizers, and external stakeholders, such as researchers and scientists.

Thanks to the leaders of the nonprofit Masgutova Foundation, including but certainly not limited to Maria Bates, George Copa, Elizabeth Forgione, Heidi Pennella, Patricia Shackleford, and all the passionate, mission-driven volunteers within the boards and committees, and those who are affiliated with the Masgutova Graduate School of NeuroDevelopmental Sciences. Much gratitude to the Lake Nona community for their support during this next growth stage.

A heartfelt thank-you to all the parents and professionals championing the Masgutova Method abroad, including teams in the Netherlands, Poland, several other European countries, the Middle East, Singapore, Indonesia, and Australia. To Elzbieta Masgutow, Teresa Busz, and Wil van Kessel, especially, I express my deepest appreciation for your hospitality and extraordinary work.

I sincerely thank those who helped with editing, including Pamela, Melanie Gall, the team at Girl Friday Productions, Christopher Hoffman, Laurie Longest, Dr. Masgutova, Nancy Morris, Isabelle, Patricia, and Allison Williams. Thanks to all those with whom I spoke and corresponded regarding specific chapter content or project scope, whether through email or by phone, including Catriona Kelly, Lewis Siegelbaum, Charles Steinwedel, and Anton Yasnitsky.

To my mom and best friend, Barbara Barnard; my sisters

and best friends, Carolyn Noble and Becky Ames; and my mother-in-law and dear friend, Charlene; and all our family members—thank you for your ongoing love and support. Dan, you are a true lifelong partner, father, helpful beta reader, and my biggest fan. Thank you for years of marriage and friendship. Dear Daniel, thank you for choosing us. You are our sun and star.

To the Sadykov family, including Nelly Akhmatova and her family, and Denis, Elzbieta, and Jan Masgutow, I have eternal gratitude for the gifts you have brought to the world.

Dear Dr. Masgutova, I am writing this letter in a blue dress. Here is a gift to you as gratitude for the wisdom and healing you have shared with my family, as well as children and adults worldwide through your MNRI/Masgutova Method. May the depth of your touch continue to be felt for generations to come. I am eternally grateful and honored for this opportunity.

Love always, Kathy

APPENDIX

*Selected MNRI Reflex Pattern Definitions

The following definitions are a very simplified summary of the reflex definition, developmental implications, and effects of non-integration based on the MNRI/Masgutova Method concepts. A more comprehensive explanation of these reflexes and reflex repatterning exercises can be found in the original sources of information: *Parents' Guide to MNRI,* by Svetlana Masgutova, PhD, and Denis Masgutov, MA, and other SMEI courses.

The SMEI and Masgutova Graduate School educational courses provide additional in-depth theoretical and practical knowledge for these reflex classifications, their developmental functions, effects of non-integration within different brain-body systems, and assisted and self-initiated exercises to facilitate integration or reintegration.

For more information on accessing these educational courses, visit www.MasgutovaMethod.com or www.MasgutovaGraduateSchool.com.

The **Asymmetrical Tonic Neck Reflex (ATNR)** supports the development of asymmetrical cross-lateral motor coordination of the core and limbs. This reflex prepares an infant for transitional movements. The ATNR influences the development of multiple cognitive systems, including auditory, auditory-visual, space and space-time orientation, and auditory perception, processing, and memory. A nonintegrated ATNR is one of the most prevalent reasons for problems in school. Effects of non-integration include lack of coordination in cross-lateral movements, trouble paying attention, auditory hypersensitivity, and learning issues.

The **Babinski Reflex** affects overall gross motor development. This is a foundational foot reflex for triggering mobility in the pelvis and sacrum, which affects the cerebrospinal fluid–pumping mechanism. This reflex affects the whole body and is key for grounding and stability. The Babinski Reflex is also used for pain management. This reflex facilitates the development and function of the peripheral and central nervous systems. Babinski Reflex integration helps with crawling, standing, running, climbing, manual skills coordination, stability, and confidence. Effects of non-integration include lack of grounding or stability, poor balance and postural control, problems with gross and fine motor coordination, and passiveness in decision-making.

The **Babkin Palmomental Reflex** is connected with eating reflexes, nourishment, and the development of mouth-palm coordination. The maturation of this reflex is foundational for the whole sensorimotor complex. Integration of this reflex also supports exploration of the body's midline and sides and affects overall space-time orientation. Effects of non-integration include addictions, poor muscle tone regulation in the upper body and oral-facial system, teeth grinding, and poor patterns of sucking, swallowing, biting, chewing, and eating.

The **Bauer Crawling Reflex** plays a crucial role in preparing an infant to walk. This reflex is theorized to support myelination of the lower motor neural pathways, which create the basis for integration in both brain hemispheres. Myelination activates the nerve net system in the corpus callosum so that both sides of the brain can communicate with each other. This reflex influences gross motor coordination and control; myelination of the pyramidal tract for facilitation of fine motor skills, language, and abstract thinking; cross-lateral movement; binocular vision and binaural hearing; multitasking; creativity; and goal-setting. Effects of non-integration include challenges with gross motor planning and control; delayed crawling; poor protection and survival mechanisms during states of stress; poor gravity, grounding, stability, and Core Tendon Guard reflexes; lack of ability to multitask; lack of creativity; and trouble setting and accomplishing goals.

The **Bonding Reflex** establishes the foundation for trust, protection, self-confidence, communication, and connection. Integration facilitates positive thinking, language development, optimism, and healthy curiosity. Effects of non-integration include codependency, poor self-identity, emotional fragility, poor stress management, fear, worry, and pessimism.

The **Foot Tendon Guard Reflex** is a protective reaction, noted in the tendons, to physical or emotional stress. This reflex affects gravity, grounding and stability, preparation for standing, motor programming, gross motor coordination, motor memory, ability to focus, emotional stability, speech articulation, and concentration. Effects of non-integration include poor regulation of gravity, grounding, and stability; difficulty standing; poor motor programming; delays in gross motor coordination; poor motor memory; challenges with focusing; emotional instability; and delays in articulation and speech development.

The **Hands Supporting Reflex** is a reflex pattern for protection and survival. This reflex supports the development of gross motor coordination of the arms and whole body. It affects the establishment of boundaries, personal space, and self-protection.

Effects of non-integration include being prone to injuries related to tripping and falling, poor personal boundaries, tendency for aggression, and information-processing difficulties.

The **Leg Cross Flexion-Extension Reflex** is a complex reflex pattern whose circuit reaches the medulla oblongata in the lowest part of the brain and lowest portion of the brain stem. The medulla oblongata transmits signals between the spinal cord and higher parts of the brain and controls autonomic activities such as heartbeat and respiration. Activation of this circuit affects neural development of the lower motor pathways and maturation of the brain stem and interbrain. This reflex influences coordination of the legs, protective responses, locomotion, cognitive development, perception, and space-time orientation. Effects of non-integration include poor neural maturation of the lower motor neurons; hyperactivity or hypoactivity; dysfunctions in crawling and walking; postural problems; excessive muscle tension; delays in crawling, sitting, and walking; slow perception; poor cognitive development; and chaotic sensory processing.

The **Spinal Perez Reflex** is foundational for whole-body coordination and development. This reflex supports efficient spine mobility, postural control, proper circulation of cerebrospinal fluid, micromovements of the cranial nerves, bladder and bowel control, detoxification, and legs-body core coordination. Proper maturation of this reflex pattern is essential for the development of our natural spinal curves. Effects of non-integration include lack of muscle-tone regulation; abnormal gait; problems with rolling, crawling, sitting, or standing; poor head control; lack of proper visual and auditory perception; poor focusing; spinal deformities; stimming; hypersensitive auditory and tactile systems; tendencies for hyperactive and impulsive behavior; and auditory-processing deficits.

The **Trunk Extension Reflex** influences the spine, development of front-back muscle coordination, and postural control. The integration of this reflex is theorized to ensure the maturation of lower motor neurons and the development of the extrapyramidal tract of the brain for conscious programming, control, language development, abstract thinking, curiosity, proper sensory processing, and feelings of confidence. This reflex prepares an infant to stand and walk. Effects of non-integration include a tendency to walk with the body leaning either too far backward or forward, toe walking, and a narrow range of perception and engagement.

EXHIBIT 1: Protective Reflex Patterns

Core Tendon Guard

The Core Tendon Guard Reflex is a protective response. This reflex sends information to the brain, where the reticular activating system and thalamus evaluate whether the stimulus is a threat. If a threat is detected, the hypothalamic pituitary adrenal (HPA) stress axis is activated and releases adrenaline, cortisol, and noradrenaline to jump-start the response to the threat.

If the Core Tendon Guard Reflex cannot cope with intense stress, then the brain-body system responds with two modes of increased protection: freezing or the fight-or-flight response. Therefore, the Core Tendon Guard Reflex facilitates a connection between the core, trunk, and limbs to help the person survive.

This reflex's response reveals itself through two modes: Red Light response or Green Light response. The type of stress determines the mode of response.

The Red Light response corresponds to freezing, which is exhibited through flexion, core withdrawal, holding of breath, visual convergence, and inhibition of movement.

The Green Light response corresponds to fight or flight, which manifests through overextension of the trunk and core muscles, visual divergence, a fight for active protection, or fleeing to escape danger.

In this way, the two responses of the Core Tendon Guard Reflex Pattern help to regulate the HPA stress-axis response.

When these protective strategies have served the short-term need, then the reflex response has accomplished its goal. The body can return to its normal state of homeostasis.

The Core Tendon Guard Reflex can be active for up to a year after an especially traumatic event. An extensive triggering of the Core Tendon Guard Reflex causes prolonged tendon and muscle contraction, as well as ongoing activation of the brain stem's protective responses. Accessing the brain's cortical functions becomes more difficult. A person also will exhibit poor posture due to frequent or long-term tension.

Fear Paralysis and Moro

The Fear Paralysis and Moro Embrace Reflex Patterns organize the protective freeze or fight-or-flight responses. They are different in both stimulus and response.

The **Fear Paralysis Reflex**, also known as the startle reflex, is triggered by a sudden auditory, visual, or tactile stimulus, such as an unexpected loud sound or uncomfortable touch. This reflex activates a sympathetic response followed by a parasympathetic response to freeze the body. Fear Paralysis can elicit the jaw muscles to clench, rapid eye blinking or pupil dilation, holding of breath, increased heart rate, and sweating. This is the basis for the "freeze" reaction, as the sympathetic nervous system is stimulated to such a degree that a person feels frozen, or unable to act. Once this protective response has accomplished its task, the body should return to a normal state of homeostasis.

Integration of this reflex helps support stress management and stress resilience, a balance between sensory and motor system activity during states of stress, postural control, emotional regulation, focusing, and information processing.

Effects of non-integration of the Fear Paralysis Reflex include anxiety, fatigue, overwhelming emotions, depression, disassociation, disintegration of sensory and motor systems in stress, problems with focusing, negative protection and survival reactions, and problems with processing information.

The **Moro Embrace Reflex**, meanwhile, is triggered by a vestibular or proprioceptive stimulation. This reflex is activated by a sudden loss of stability or change in head position due to a swift shift in the body's gravity line, such as during a fall. The sudden loss of stability prompts the limbs to move from the core to the periphery and then from the periphery back to the core. This reflex pattern can help prevent a fall.

The Moro is associated with the first breath of life.

The integration of the Moro supports the release of fear and anxiety being interpreted by the thalamus, amygdala, and insula, enabling a person to perceive more possibilities and to invite courage into their lives. Moro exercises release shock and negative protection responses. An integrated Moro also helps coordinate the function of breathing, visual and auditory focusing, creativity, and integration of thought and movement.

Effects of non-integration include excessive anxiety, adrenal fatigue, motion sickness, fear of taking risks, emotional instability, phobias (uncontrollable, irrational, and persistent fears of a certain situation), improper protection and survival responses, hyperactivity or hypersensitivity, lack of courage or trust, fear of change, compromised immunity, poor focusing, irrational behavior, and poor coordination between thought and movement.

EXHIBIT 2: Core MNRI Programs of the Svetlana Masgutova Educational Institute and Master of Science Degree at the Not-for-Profit Masgutova Graduate School of NeuroDevelopmental Sciences

Dr. Masgutova has developed an extensive MNRI program, with each course addressing a specific aspect of functional development. Inclusive specialized techniques aim to improve body function and the integration of primary motor-reflex patterns. Many of these courses offer continuing education credits (CEUs). The following is a list of some of the courses offered through the US-based Svetlana Masgutova Educational Institute:

- MNRI Archetype Movement Integration
- MNRI Dynamic and Postural Reflex Integration
- MNRI Lifelong Reflex Integration
- MNRI NeuroTactile Integration
- MNRI NeuroStructural Integration
- MNRI Parent Workshop
- MNRI Reflex Integration: Maximizing Brain Potential
- MNRI Stress and Trauma Recovery
- MNRI Toolbox for Dyslexia
- MNRI Oral-Facial Reflex Integration Levels 1 and 2
- MNRI Proprioceptive and Cognitive Integration
- MNRI Upper Limbs Reflex and Manual Skill Integration
- MNRI Visual and Auditory Reflexes Integration
- MNRI Introduction to Intronauts and Infant Reflexes Integration
- MNRI NeuroTactile, Primary Motor and Reflex Integration (Advanced)
- MNRI Reflex Integration for Newborns
- MNRI Stress Hormones and Reflex Integration
- MNRI Aqua Reflex Integration

- MNRI Basal Ganglia Reflex Integration
- MNRI Breathing Reflex Integration
- MNRI Children with Challenges Reflex Integration
- MNRI Dysfunctional and Pathological Repatterning and Integration
- MNRI Introduction to Reflex Integration for Epilepsy
- MNRI Introduction to Reflex Neuromodulation for Concussion Recovery

For more information, visit www.MasgutovaMethod.com.

Masgutova Graduate School of NeuroDevelopmental Sciences: The graduate school is a not-for-profit higher-education institution that is part of the Masgutova Foundation. Founded in 2020, the MGS offers a cutting-edge master of science degree that empowers graduates with quality research skills and the theoretical and practical knowledge of neuroreflex integration and neuromodulation. The following is a list of some of the courses offered through the Masgutova Graduate School:

- Anatomy, Neuroanatomy and Neurophysiology for Reflex Neuromodulation
- Primary Movement and Biomechanics Integration
- Reflex Maturation for Physical, Emotional, and Cognitive Development
- Neurodevelopment, Neuro-Immunology and Reflex Neuromodulation
- Neuromodulation of Infant and Toddler Reflexes
- Introduction to Neuro-Embryology and Brain Development

For more information, visit www.MasgutovaFoundation.org and www.MasgutovaGraduateSchool.com.

EXHIBIT 3: Primitive and Primary Reflexes

Dr. Masgutova has been developing her method and techniques primarily based on the works of physiologists including Sechenov, Pavlov, Sherrington, and Luria, and psychologists such as Vygotsky and Jean Piaget, whose concepts of reflex as a specific phenomenon of the central nervous system often differ from what traditional literature may present. The MNRI/Masgutova Method distinguishes between primitive and primary reflexes. Based on more than thirty years of clinical observations, application, and theory, the MNRI considers the encoded reflex developmental dynamic according to the following timeline:

> **Between 0 and 28 days and up to 2 months:** The appearance (reflexes emerge prior to birth, in utero) of the reflex occurs for the first time under the gravity condition immediately after birth. This is considered its "chaotic" expression, as characterized by its unconditioned, involuntary, and pure rigid automaticity stage. The prominent expression of the primitive pattern in the first weeks of life up to 2 months at the latest is a stress response from the intense process of birth and possible birth trauma.
>
> This stage of the primitive reflex creates the bridge from the prenatal and birthing reflexes to the primary phase of the reflex. It is an adaptive/transitive phase necessary to cope with post-birth stress and adapt to the new post-birth environment. This stage initiates proper connections between sensory and motor biomechanics under terrestrial conditions and is theorized to assure continuity between the intrauterine level of myelination and postnatal primary myelination.

Between 28 days and 2 to 4 months: The reflex pattern transitions from the primitive to primary stage. This stage of the primary reflex paves the three parts of the sensorimotor circuit, establishes proper reflex biomechanics, and paves fluid nerve networks for specific stimulation. In this stage, the coding of the unconditioned reflex continues. The sensory field becomes more well defined. The connection between the sensory input and the motor response establishes a clear sensorimotor circuit.

This stage is a critical time for early intervention and optimizing the developmental trajectory of any baby, whether they are born with challenges or present as neurotypical. The prominent expression of the primitive pattern in the first 2 months is a stress response from the dynamic process of birth. The goal is to not allow infants to be "stuck" in that stage.

The primitive reflexes must progress and be patterned to the primary basic reflex phase during this critical time frame as fast as possible; otherwise, the primitive reflexes will block further neurodevelopment. The MNRI/Masgutova Method promotes the maturation of the infant's reflexes to their primary expression according to the natural schedule of their developmental dynamic. This is the only way for the reflexes to reach full integration and support higher functions such as abilities and skills.

The neurophysiologically sensitive time frame of the 0-to-4-month stage represents the reflex's primary function as a survival and protective response.

4 months to 6 months: This stage signifies the beginning of the transition[83] from the unconditioned basic pattern to the conditioned variant pattern.

6 months to 12 months: The reflex continues (and completes) its maturation as a conditioned pattern under the influence of learning processes and experiences. It assumes more variant patterns as it becomes more voluntary-movement based.

The 4-to-12-month stage represents the intentional response of the reflex. By the end of the first year, 70–75 percent of reflexes have developed through the unconditioned-transition-conditioned period of primary reflex integration.

15 months and beyond: The reflex has integrated and supports complex abilities and skills. The first 15 months are crucial for proper myelination of the reflex circuit. The MNRI Method theorizes that proper myelination is directly linked to the maturation of the reflex circuit. Proper myelination of axons supports a reflex circuit's electrical conductivity and action potential. Therefore, delays in reflex maturation impede the myelination of a reflex circuit.

Learning, planning, and developing internal control are essential functions of the brain's cortex. Development of these skills depends on the physiological maturation of the brain stem and the diencephalon (as governed by the myelination of the extrapyramidal nerve net) through the early movements and neurosensorimotor integration that are foundational for human development.

Immature reflex patterns, theorized to be linked with poor paving of the nerve pathways and myelination of the sensorimotor pathways, cannot support higher-level cortical functions and visual skills.

Therefore, maladaptive mechanisms and neurodevelopmental disorders may occur if these reflexes have not properly matured and integrated.

—S. Masgutova, D. Masgutov, and N. Akhmatova

EXHIBIT 4: The Masgutova Method's Stages of Grief and Emotional Recovery Protocol

Each of these includes a specific exercise protocol to facilitate reflex integration. Grief and emotional recovery exercises are offered through the Masgutova Foundation, along with other neuroreflex exercise protocols to support health, well-being, and reflex integration.

Stage 1: Shock and Denial
Stage 2: Pain and Guilt
Stage 3: Anger and Bargaining
Stage 4: Depression and Loneliness
Stage 5: Reflection and Upward Turn
Stage 6: Reconstruction and Working Through
Stage 7: Acceptance and Hope

For more information, visit www.MasgutovaFoundation.org.

EXHIBIT 5: Overview of the Masgutova Method's Levels of Tactility Concepts

Dr. Masgutova's and Denis's particular interest was tactility, as expressed by the development of a five-level system designed to support neurodevelopment. Primary tactility response is interpreted in the MNRI Method as a reflex and defined as the generalized response of the skin-tactile and body-brain systems to the context of touch: safe or unsafe, and pleasant or unpleasant. Individualized MNRI NeuroTactile techniques target the specific sensory receptors that are a priority for processing the tactile information at each of the five levels.

The first four levels target the extrapyramidal nervous system and subcortical structures of the brain responsible for the development and maturation of automatic processes of the body-brain system. The fifth level, differentiated tactility, reaches the pyramidal system, bringing cortical awareness of sensation and the ability to differentiate and communicate the different qualities of touch.

Generalized tactility represents the body's general perception and sensation of touch. Generalized, or primary, tactility occurs during pregnancy when the fetus develops under the pressure of amniotic fluid and space within the mother's uterus. The birthing canal squeeze activates the cranial bones and rib cage to support life after a natural birthing process. A natural birth switches on the breathing and eating functions and establishes the Bonding Reflex* Pattern.

Generalized tactility supports the integration of all body receptors for health and normal functioning and overall neurodevelopment, including one's perception of the internal and external worlds.

Generalized tactility deprivation can cause poor links in

the body's receptors, dysregulation in homeostasis and perception in one's internal-external world, dysregulation of stress hormones and the HPA stress axis, and overall discomfort in the body.

Protective tactility, which is also a generalized response, is an encoded ability of the brain to alert the body about any kind of touch that represents a potential danger. This tactility level triggers the body's internal alarm and the activation of the sympathetic system to keep the body safe. The brain evaluates any stimulus based on its degree of safety.

Generalized protective tactility supports the regulation of the HPA stress axis, determines the level of stress hormone release required to address the acute or chronic stress, and prepares the body to activate all the systems required to mobilize into the freeze or fight-or-flight stages.

A deprivation of protective tactility may result in poor connectivity in the brain and improper freeze or fight-or-flight responses, an overworked HPA stress axis, anxiety, and dysregulation of stress hormones.

Dermatome tactility is a skin sensation felt through the spinal nerves. This third level of tactility trains the sympathetic and whole nervous system for proper functioning, links the peripheral and central nervous systems, trains the ability for differentiated touch in a generalized manner, and supports programming and control of muscular-tendinous tone, posture, and movements.

Dermatome tactility deprivation results in insufficient sympathetic and whole nervous system functioning; poor connection between the peripheral and central nervous systems; poor support of programming and control in muscle tone, posture, and movements; an overworked HPA stress axis; and hypoactive and hyperreactive reflexes.

Reflex tactility elicits receptors associated with reflexes such as Babkin Palmomental, Robinson Hands Grasp, Babinski, and Automatic Gait. Reflex tactility addresses specific receptors activated by external stimuli and how the spinal cord and brain interpret them.

Specific receptors in certain zones activate a particular response when interacting with the reflex circuits. Reflex tactility activates and regulates the body's response within the reflex circuit(s), affects reflex differentiation, controls the freeze or fight-or-flight responses, connects with the HPA stress axis, and trains the body through its sensorimotor developmental milestones.

Reflex tactility deprivation causes poor regulation of the reflex circuit functions and their components, poor reflex differentiation that results in mixed and dysfunctional responses, dysfunction in the automatic control of the freeze or fight-or-flight responses, poor connectivity with the HPA stress axis, and poor development of sensorimotor milestones.

Differentiated tactility enables a person to discriminate between the qualities of any object or recipient of their touch voluntarily and consciously. Differentiated tactility supports the functioning of the somatosensory system, which evaluates touch, pressure, pain, temperature, position, movement, and vibration. These elements arise from the muscles, joints, skin, and fascia; control the freeze and fight-or-flight responses; and support the connectivity of the sensory cortex and protective brain structures (subcortical and brain stem) and functions of reflexes and the HPA stress axis. This tactility level also trains the body for sensorimotor development milestones.

Differentiated tactility deprivation causes a lack of integration and confusion in a person's interpretation of touch, pressure, pain, temperature, position, movement, and vibration; produces a lack of control in the freeze and fight-or-flight responses; results in poor connectivity in the sensory cortex and protective brain structures and functions of reflexes and the HPA stress axis; and produces poor support of programming and control of posture and movements.

NOTES

1 See the appendix for the Masgutova Method definition. Refer to the appendix for selected reflex references marked with an asterisk.
2 Hoagwood, K. E., Olin, S. S., Wang, N. M., Pollock, M., Acri, M., Glaeser, E., Whitmyre, E. D., Storfer-Isser, A., & Horwitz, S. M. (2017). Developing a sustainable child and family service system after a community tragedy: Lessons from Sandy Hook. *Journal of Community Psychology*, 45(6), 748–764. https://doi.org/10.1002/jcop.21890
3 Masgutova, S. (2016). Post-trauma recovery in children of Newtown, CT, using MNRI reflex integration. *Journal of Traumatic Stress Disorders & Treatment*, 5(5). https://doi.org/10.4172/2324-8947.1000163
4 Svetlana Masgutova Educational Institute. (n.d.). *About us*. https://masgutovamethod.com/about-the-svetlana-masgutova-educational-institute
5 *Reflexes: Portal to Neurodevelopment and Learning* was a significant reference and inspiration for the biography. This book provides numerous testimonials of the effect of MNRI on individuals with different neurodeficits and/or who have experienced traumatic events.
6 We had intended on traveling to Russia, but the borders closed two days prior to our scheduled arrival, due to the coronavirus pandemic. As of the time of this book's publishing, travel between the US and Russia still was heavily restricted.
7 Keller, B. (1989, June 5). 500 on 2 trains reported killed by

Soviet gas pipeline explosion. *The New York Times*. https://www.nytimes.com/1989/06/05/world/500-on-2-trains-reported-killed-by-soviet-gas-pipeline-explosion.html

8 Masgutova, S., & Masgutov, D. (2015). You are a winner. *Reflexes: Portal to neurodevelopment and learning: A collective work* (p. 531). Svetlana Masgutova Educational Institute for Neuro-Sensory-Motor and Reflex Integration.

9 Masgutova, S., & Masgutov, D. (2015). *Reflexes: Portal to neurodevelopment and learning: A collective work* (p. 531). Svetlana Masgutova Educational Institute for Neuro-Sensory-Motor and Reflex Integration.

10 A reflex integration platform is the appropriate name for what looks like a massage table. It's often used during reflex and neurosensorimotor exercises.

11 Best Countries 2019. *U.S. News and World Report*. https://www.usnews.com/media/best-countries/overall-rankings-2019.pdf

12 The famous Shulgan-Tash (Kapova) cave is one of the largest caves in the Southern Urals, with more than 150 Paleolithic cave drawings of global importance having been discovered, including drawings of mammoths, horses, rhinoceroses, bulls, and abstract characters in red ocher. Radiochemical analysis indicates that the Shulgan-Tash drawings are about thirteen to fourteen thousand years old. According to the United Nations Educational, Scientific and Cultural Organization, the cave art of Shulgan-Tash represents a masterpiece of human genius. Such antique cave art has been otherwise only discovered in France and Spain. *Bashkir Ural*. UNESCO World Heritage Convention. https://whc.unesco.org/en/tentativelists/5666/

13 Pelenski, J. (1967). Muscovite imperial claims to the Kazan Khanate. *Slavic Review*, 26(4), 559–576. https://doi.org/10.2307/2492609

14 1939 Census, per *Wikipedia,* https://en.wikipedia.org/wiki/Bashkortostan. More than one hundred nationalities are represented in the Bashkir Republic now. The state symbols of what is now the Republic of Bashkortostan include a combination of symbols and emblems reflecting the historical, state, and other traditions of the republic, its economy, geographical location, intellectual potential, and spiritual life. https://www.bashkortostan.ru/republic/

15 Pipes, R. E. (1950). The first experiment in Soviet national policy: The Bashkir Republic, 1917–1920. *The Russian Review,* 9(4), 303–319. https://doi.org/10.2307/125989

16 *Gulag,* History.com, March 23, 2018. https://www.history.com/topics/russia/gulag; DiDuca, M. (2016). *Russia: Insight guide* (p. 58). Apa Publications.

17 Miyakinsky District of the Republic of Bashkortostan. Labor and combat deeds of Miyakinites during the Great Patriotic War. http://www.miaki.ru/history/podvigi_miakinzev.html

18 Kelly, C. (2007). *Children's world: Growing up in Russia, 1890–1991* (pp. 534, 541). Yale University Press.

19 Even though the battles in the Great Patriotic War didn't take place in their part of the country directly, the Urals became a haven of evacuation and refuge: "And so, they sought to keep their body and soul together at home, they did their bit to repair the damage elsewhere." All told, at least twenty-seven million Soviet people died. Of those who survived, about thirty-five million were left homeless. Dukes, P. (2015). *A history of the Urals: Russia's crucible from the early empire to the post-Soviet era* (p. 141). Bloomsbury Publishing.

20 Kozlov, D., & Gilburd, E. (2013). Introduction. *The thaw: Society and culture during the 1950s and 1960s.* University of Toronto Press, Scholarly Publishing Division.

21 Ascher, A. (2017). *Russia: A short history: Revised edition* (pp. 225–227). Oneworld Publications.

22 This city was named Kujbyšev from 1935 to 1991. It was then renamed Samara. *Samara. Encyclopedia Britannica.* Retrieved September 6, 2022, from https://www.britannica.com/place/Samara-Russia

23 This book references her by first name throughout her childhood and until she received her PhD.

24 Kelly, C. (2007). *Children's world: Growing up in Russia, 1890–1991* (p. 570). Yale University Press; Kozlov, D., & Gilburd, E. (2013). *The thaw: Soviet society and culture during the 1950s and 1960s* (pp. 8–9). University of Toronto Press.

25 *USSR: Nationality units of territorial administration.* (1962, June 1). Library of Congress. https://www.loc.gov/resource/g7001f.ct002986/?r=0.077,0.06,0.643,0.348,0

26 Tolstoy, L. (2012). *Leo Tolstoy's fables for children* (pp. 138–139). Translated from the original Russian of 1904 and edited by Leo Wiener. Dana Estes. https://publicdomainreview.org/collections/leo-tolstoys-fables-for-children-1904/

27 Wild food plants especially were the subject of intense emphasis for diet during the Great Patriotic War, most notably during the siege of Leningrad in 1941–1944. Shikov, A. N., Tsitsilin, A. N., Pozharitskaya, O., Makarov, V. G., & Michael Heinrich. (2017, November 21). Traditional and current food use of wild plants listed in the Russian pharmacopoeia. *Frontiers in Pharmacology.* National Center for Biotechnology Information. https://www.ncbi.nlm.nih.gov/pmc/articles/PMC5702350/

28 Haas, L. F. (1998). Ivan Mikhailovich Sechenov (1829–1905). *Journal of Neurology, Neurosurgery & Psychiatry, 65*(4), 554. https://doi.org/10.1136/jnnp.65.4.554

29 Stuart, D. G., Schaefer, A. T., Massion, J., Graham, B. A., & Callister, R. J. (2014). Pioneers in CNS inhibition: 1. Ivan M. Sechenov, the first to clearly demonstrate inhibition arising in the brain. *Brain Research,* 1548, 20–48. https://doi.org/10.1016/j.brainres.2013.12.006

30 Bann, T. A. (2018, March 29). *Neuropsychopharmacology in historical perspective education in the field in the post-neuropsychopharmacology era: Sechenov's re-evaluation of mental faculties and the brain* (Bulletin 11). Retrieved February 3, 2023, from https://inhn.org/about/central-office-cordoba-unit/education/thomas-a-ban-neuropsychopharmacology-in-historical-perspective-education-in-the-field-in-the-post-neuropsychopharmacology-era/bulletin-11-sechenovs-re-evaluation-of-mental-faculties-and-the-brain

31 *Claude Bernard.* (n.d.). Famous Scientists. Retrieved September 6, 2022, from https://www.famousscientists.org/claude-bernard/

32 Willis described the various parts of the brain, including the cerebral cortex and the basal ganglia.

33 Clarac, F. (2012, December 15). *The history of reflexes, part 1: From Descartes to Pavlov.* IBRO History of Neuroscience. http://ibro.org/wp-content/uploads/2018/07/The-History-of-Reflexes-Part-1.pdf

34 Svetlana Masgutova Educational Institute. *Ivan Mikhailovich Sechenov.* Additional credits and further reading are referenced in her research. See also the appendix. http://masgutovamethod.com/_uploads/_media_uploads/_source/mm_scholars_sechenov.pdf

35 Stuart, D. G., Schaefer, A. T., Massion, J., Graham, B. A., & Callister, R. J. (2014). Pioneers in CNS inhibition: 1. Ivan M. Sechenov, the first to clearly demonstrate inhibition arising in the brain. *Brain Research, 1548,* 20–48. https://doi.org/10.1016/j.brainres.2013.12.006

36 Lawson, B. R., Graham, J. E., & Baker, K. (2007). *A history of psychology: Globalization, ideas, and applications* (p. 400). Pearson Education.

37 *Reflexes of the brain.* (2022, October 20). MIT Press. Retrieved February 3, 2023, from https://mitpress.mit.edu/9780262690065/reflexes-of-the-brain/

38 McLeish, J. (1975, 2017). *Soviet psychology: History, theory, content: The origin of objective psychology. (i) Ivan Mikhailovich Sechenov (1829–1905).* Routledge; Stuart, D. G., Schaefer, A. T., Massion, J., Graham, B. A., & Callister, R. J. (2014). Pioneers in CNS inhibition: 1. Ivan M. Sechenov, the first to clearly demonstrate inhibition arising in the brain. *Brain Research, 1548,* 29. https://doi.org/10.1016/j.brainres.2013.12.006
39 Todes, D. P. (1984). Biological psychology and the Tsarist censor: The dilemma of scientific development. *Bulletin of the History of Medicine, 58*(4), 529–544. https://tinyurl.com/msk439b8
40 Svetlana Masgutova Educational Institute. *Ivan Mikhailovich Sechenov.* https://masgutovamethod.com/the-method/scientific-background
41 McLeish, J. (1975, 2017). *Soviet psychology: History, theory, content: The origin of objective psychology. (i) Ivan Mikhailovich Sechenov (1829–1905).* Routledge.
42 *Life and theater of Karim Tinchurin.* (2012, September 15). Republic of Tatarstan. http://rt-online.ru/p-rubr-kult-68484/
43 The Nuremberg trials were a series of trials held between 1945 and 1946 in Nuremberg, Germany, to bring Nazi war criminals to justice for genocide and crimes against humanity. Great Britain, France, the United States, and the Soviet Union presided over the trials, for which there was no other international precedent yet established. *Nuremberg trials.* (2010, January 29). History.com. Retrieved September 6, 2022, from https://www.history.com/topics/world-war-ii/nuremberg-trials
44 About 15 percent of the world's population, or an estimated one in six people, lives with disabilities. They compose the largest global minority. United Nations. (n.d.). *Factsheet on persons with disabilities.* Retrieved February 15, 2023, from https://www.un.org/development/desa/disabilities/resources/factsheet-on-persons-with-disabilities.html

45 Fontaine, I. R. (2017). Effect of reflex neuromodulation on an infant with severe amniotic band syndrome: A case report on the use of MNRI techniques for physical therapy. *International Journal of Neurorehabilitation, 4*(1). https://doi.org/10.4172/2376-0281.1000248

46 Schmidt, N. B., Richey, J. A., Zvolensky, M. J., & Maner, J. K. (2008). Exploring human freeze responses to a threat stressor. *Journal of Behavior Therapy and Experimental Psychiatry, 39*(3), 292–304. https://doi.org/10.1016/j.jbtep.2007.08.002

47 Masgutova, S. (n.d.). *What can make reflexes dysfunctional.* Svetlana Masgutova Educational Institute. Retrieved September 6, 2022, from https://masgutovamethod.com/the-method/what-can-make-reflexes-dysfunctional

48 Masgutova, S. (2016). Post-trauma recovery in children of Newtown, CT, using MNRI reflex integration. *Journal of Traumatic Stress Disorders & Treatment, 5*(5). https://doi.org/10.4172/2324-8947.1000163

49 Masgutova, S., & Masgutov, D. (2015). Reflex integration for post-trauma survival and recovery. *Reflexes: Portal to neurodevelopment and learning: A collective work* (p. 71). Svetlana Masgutova Educational Institute for Neuro-Sensory-Motor and Reflex Integration.

50 On this day: Ufa train disaster. (2019, June 4). *The Moscow Times.* https://www.themoscowtimes.com/2019/06/04/on-this-day-ufa-train-disaster-a65865

51 Masgutova, S., & Masgutov, D. (2015). You are a winner. *Reflexes: Portal to neurodevelopment and learning: A collective work* (p. 531). Svetlana Masgutova Educational Institute for Neuro-Sensory-Motor and Reflex Integration.

52 Masgutova, S., & Masgutov, D. (2015). You are a winner. *Reflexes: Portal to neurodevelopment and learning: A collective work* (p. 527). Svetlana Masgutova Educational Institute for Neuro-Sensory-Motor and Reflex Integration.

53 Masgutova, S., & Masgutov, D. (2015). You are a winner.

Reflexes: Portal to neurodevelopment and learning: A collective work (p. 529). Svetlana Masgutova Educational Institute for Neuro-Sensory-Motor and Reflex Integration.

54 Rieber, R. W. (1998). *The collected works of L. S. Vygotsky, vol. 5: Child psychology* (pp. 147, 196, 242).

55 *Lev Semyonovich Vygotsky.* (n.d.). Svetlana Masgutova Educational Institute. http://masgutovamethod.com/_uploads/_media_uploads/_source/mm_scholars_vygotsky.pdf

56 IAEA. (2016, November 7). *Frequently asked Chernobyl questions.* Retrieved February 3, 2023, from https://www.iaea.org/newscenter/focus/chernobyl/faqs

57 Masgutova, S., & Masgutov, D. (2017). *MNRI: Post-trauma recovery* (pp. 99–117). Svetlana Masgutova Educational Institute for Neuro-Sensory-Motor and Reflex Integration.

58 Masgutova, S., & Masgutov, D. (2017). *MNRI: Post-trauma recovery* (pp. 6–7). Svetlana Masgutova Educational Institute for Neuro-Sensory-Motor and Reflex Integration.

59 Masgutova, S., & Masgutov, D. (2018). MNRI archetype movement integration. *Explore the biomechanics of primary motor pattern (IPET)* (pp. 26–29). Svetlana Masgutova Educational Institute.

60 Masgutova, S., & Curlee, P. (2004, 2007, 2012). *You are a winner* (p. 61). 1st World Publishing.

61 Masgutova, S., & Masgutov, D. (2015). You are a winner. *Reflexes: Portal to neurodevelopment and learning: A collective work* (p. 535). Svetlana Masgutova Educational Institute for Neuro-Sensory-Motor and Reflex Integration.

62 Masgutova, S., & Curlee, P. (2004, 2007, 2012). *You are a winner* (p. 59). 1st World Publishing.

63 Akhmatova, A. (1961). Requiem. (Cigale, A., Trans.). *The Hopkins Review* 9(3), 339–347 (2016). https://doi.org/10.1353/thr.2016.0076

64 Biryukova, E., & Sirotkina, I. (2020). Forward to Bernstein: Movement complexity as a new frontier.

Frontiers in Neuroscience, 14, 553. https://doi.org/10.3389/fnins.2020.00553

65 Roby-Brami, A., & Goasdoué, R. (2010). A historical perspective on learning: The legacy and actuality of I. M. Pavlov and N. A. Bernstein. *Rethinking physical and rehabilitation medicine* (pp. 71–93). https://doi.org/10.1007/978-2-8178-0034-9_4; Morasso, P. (2022). A vexing question in motor control: The degrees of freedom problem. *Frontiers in Bioengineering and Biotechnology, 9*, 783501. https://doi.org/10.3389/fbioe.2021.783501

66 This is known as the Bernstein problem. *Nikolai Bernstein.* (n.d.). Psychology Wiki. Retrieved September 6, 2022, from https://psychology.wikia.org/wiki/Nikolai_Bernstein

67 The degrees of freedom vary somewhat depending on the groups of scientists approaching the topic of the biomechanics of the human hand and its kinematic analysis. Jaworski, L., & Karpiński, R. (2017). Biomechanics of the human hand. *Journal of Technology and Exploitation in Mechanical Engineering, 3*(1), 28–33. http://yadda.icm.edu.pl/yadda/element/bwmeta1.element.baztech-0aeb0740-a637-41e4-b00e-2046b6652518/c/jaworski1.pdf; ElKoura, G., & Singh, K. (2003). Handrix: Animating the human hand. University of Toronto. http://www.dgp.toronto.edu/~gelkoura/noback/scapaper03.pdf

68 Jaworski, L., & Karpiński, R. (2017). Biomechanics of the human hand. *Journal of Technology and Exploitation in Mechanical Engineering, 3*(1), 28–33. http://yadda.icm.edu.pl/yadda/element/bwmeta1.element.baztech-0aeb0740-a637-41e4-b00e-2046b6652518/c/jaworski1.pdf

69 Masgutova, S. (1990). *Psychological assistance for children in extreme events: Active forms and method of the work of the practical psychologist.* General and Developmental Psychology Research Institute of Russian Education Academy. Russian version.

70 Masgutova, S. (1988). Looking at myself—The inner world of the teenager. *Family and School Journal,* (6). Russian version.

71 *Baku pogrom a typical example of real genocide against Armenians—eyewitness.* (2020, January 15). Armenpress. Retrieved September 6, 2022, from https://armenpress.am/eng/news/1001449.html

72 Masgutova, S. (2016, October 21). Post-trauma recovery in children of Newtown, CT, using MNRI reflex integration. *Journal of Traumatic Stress Disorders & Treatment.* Retrieved September 6, 2022, from https://www.scitechnol.com/peer-review/posttrauma-recovery-in-children-of-newtownct-using-mnri-reflex-integration-2LcJ.php?article_id=5522

73 Hoefnagel, D., & Lüders, D. (1962, 1 April). Ernst Moro (1874–1951). *Pediatrics, 29*(4), 643–645. https://pediatrics.aappublications.org/content/29/4/643

74 Masgutova, S. (2016). Post-trauma recovery in children of Newtown, CT, using MNRI reflex integration. *Journal of Traumatic Stress Disorders & Treatment, 5*(5). https:/doi.org/10.4172/2324-8947.1000163

75 Through the years, she expanded this exercise by adding tapping on the ends of the triceps muscles, at the upper end of the fascia lata, and on the ends of the deltoid muscles on both arms.

76 Scientists from the University of São Paulo and Harvard University say stress may cause a change in hair color and skin. Their research examined the stress levels in mice. Higher levels of cortisol and adrenaline caused by pain elevated the heartbeat and blood pressure, which affected the nervous system and caused acute stress. This process accelerated the depletion of stem cells that produced melanin in hair follicles. *Scientists discover "why stress turns hair white."* (2020). BBC. https://www.bbc.com/news/health-51208972

77 Mcleod, S. (2022, August 18). Lev Vygotsky's sociocultural

theory of cognitive development. *Simply Psychology.* Retrieved February 5, 2023, from https://www.simplypsychology.org /vygotsky.html

78 *Vygotsky, Lev.* (2018, July 3). New World Encyclopedia. Retrieved June 14, 2022, from https://www.newworld encyclopedia.org/p/index.php?title=Lev_Vygotsky& oldid=1012862

79 Masgutova, S., & Masgutov, D. (2015). MNRI Assessment for Determining the Level of Reflex Development. *Reflexes: Portal to neurodevelopment and learning: A collective work* (p. 201). Svetlana Masgutova Educational Institute for Neuro-Sensory-Motor and Reflex Integration.

80 Novak, K., Sobaniec, P., Sobaniec, W., Akhmatova, N., & Shackleford, P. (2020). Evaluation of the therapeutic effect of MNRI reflex neuromodulation on children diagnosed with autism based on reflex assessments, QEEG analysis, and ATEC questionnaire. *The Journal of Neurology and Neurobiology, 6*(2). https://doi.org/10.16966/2379-7150.165

81 The full list of scientific articles can be found at www .MasgutovaMethod.com—*Learn More.* https://masgutova method.com/articles#dv.i58

82 As of publication, MNRI was involved in various scientific research projects, including new QEEG brain mapping studies to examine the before-and-after effects of MNRI during educational conferences and California-based 2M Foundation's "circle of change" that aims to broaden the definition of ASD and restructure the landscape of treatments, supports, and services based on longitudinal data. Additionally, MNRI is part of Epidemic Answers/ Documenting Hope's FLIGHT Study, which aims to document and analyze a personalized, comprehensive model of whole-child care that can effectively address many chronic childhood health conditions.

83 Not all reflexes follow the same developmental timeline.

ABOUT SVETLANA MASGUTOVA, PHD, CREATOR OF THE MNRI®/ MASGUTOVA METHOD®

Photo by Naida Gazdick

Svetlana Masgutova, PhD, is a world-renowned authority on reflex integration and neurodevelopment. Dr. Masgutova is an active founder of the US-based Svetlana Masgutova Educational Institute for Neuro-Sensory-Motor and Reflex Integration, LLC, a global organization, and the International Dr. Svetlana Masgutova Institute in Poland. She is the founder and lecturer of the US-based nonprofit Masgutova Graduate School of NeuroDevelopmental Sciences. She is a member of the Lake Nona Performance Club's Medical Advisory Council. Since 1989, Dr. Masgutova has been leading research and has studied the influence of primary neurosensory-motor reflex patterns on different aspects of neurodevelopment and learning. Her work focuses on the concepts of reflex integration processes to facilitate sensory processing, motor-physical and sensory-motor rehabilitation, emotional and post-trauma recovery, and education and neurodevelopmental enrichment. Dr. Masgutova earned a PhD in psychology in 1988 in Russia. She also received a post-graduate degree in clinical neuro-speech development in Poland. She has authored more than two hundred published works on psychology, education, neurosensorimotor reflex integration, and sensorimotor-based development. For more information, please visit www.MasgutovaMethod.com or www.MasgutovaGraduateSchool.com.

ABOUT THE WRITER

Photo by Naida Gazdick

Kathryn Carr is a proud parent of an MNRI® child and an award-winning print journalist. She has served as a longtime project editor and writer for *Crain's Cleveland Business,* a weekly business newspaper that is part of Crain Communications, one of the largest privately held business media publishers in the world. She also is a contributing editor for the Svetlana Masgutova Educational Institute. During her journalism career, Kathryn oversaw the editorial team as the managing editor for *Edible Cleveland,* which was named one of Ohio's top magazines. Her work has appeared in *Cleveland Magazine, Edible Northeast Florida,* and *Palate* magazine. She also was a copy editor and designer for the *Pensacola News Journal (Fl.)* and collaborated on a newsroom reporting project that was nominated for a Pulitzer Prize. She earned a master of fine arts degree in journalism from Kent State University in Ohio.

Kathryn and her family live in northeast Florida. She is passionate about helping to advance the awareness and visibility of the MNRI/Masgutova Method.

Printed in the USA
CPSIA information can be obtained
at www.ICGtesting.com
LVHW040930250823
756185LV00001BA/1